ATLANTA'S
ICONIC
APE

Cover photo: Willie B. by Chisato Abe.

ATLANTA'S ICONIC APE

The Life of Willie B.

TERRY L. MAPLE, PH.D.

Elizabeth Smithgall-Watts Professor Emeritus,
Georgia Institute of Technology
Director of Wildlife Wellness,
Jacksonville Zoo and Gardens
Scholar-in-Residence, University of North Florida

Charleston, SC
www.PalmettoPublishing.com

Atlanta's Iconic Ape
Copyright © 2021 by Terry L. Maple, Ph.D.

Red Leaf Press, Fernandina Beach, FL.
In collaboration with Palmetto Publications Group, Charleston, SC, and Amazon/
KDP publications services.

Hardcover: 978-1-63837-072-7
Paperback: 978-1-63837-073-4
eBook: 978-1-63837-074-1

DEDICATION

This book is dedicated to the memory of CPA Terry Gordon and Professor Robert Sommer. Terry taught me how to read a balance sheet and manage scarce resources in a crisis. Bob's timeless ideas provided the programmatic blueprint for Zoo Atlanta's remarkable transformation from an industry pariah to global leadership. Sound business practices and visionary exhibit design were the keys to our recovery and the benchmarks of the legacy we share.

Rest in Peace, Terry and Bob. We miss you.

TABLE OF CONTENTS

Evelyn and Merrill Maple at the entrance of
the San Diego Zoo (T. L. Maple).

ACKNOWLEDGMENTS

My mother and father, Evelyn and Merrill Maple, introduced me to great apes and the world's greatest collection of wildlife at the San Diego Zoo when I was just a boy. The photograph above depicts them at the life-size sculpture of the male mountain gorilla Ngagi, who was exhibited at the zoo with his cagemate Mbongo in 1931. I first visited the sculpture when I was in the first grade, never knowing that I would one day commission a gorilla sculpture of my own. Although I was never employed by the San Diego Zoo, I am grateful to many colleagues at the zoo who worked with me on primate projects during the length of my career. Because there were many workshops and conferences sponsored by San Diego, I was able to visit my home town frequently on business. Years later, Atlanta has become an equally active mecca for primatologists. The late Carolyn Boyd Hatcher and Professor Richard K. Davenport provided early inspiration and encouragement as I dared to think big about the future of behavioral primatology at the zoo. My close faculty friends at Tech, Edward H. Loveland, M. J. Marr, Bryan Norton, Anderson D. Smith, and Lawrence James counseled me during the toughest moments of my reform administration.

For their sustained participation in our successful experiment in privatization, I thank Charlie Davis, Terry Gordon, Terry Harps, Lhew Haden, Robert M. Holder, Robert C. Petty, Clare Richardson, and three decades of dedicated service from the Atlanta corporate community. Attending veterinarians Mike Keeling, M. S. Silberman, Brent Swenson, Rita McManamon, and a keeper team led by Charles Horton nursed Willie B. through many health challenges as he matured. The generous support of the Charles and Celestia Smithgall family, the family of Jay Crouse, the family of Deen Day Smith/Sanders, the John Bulow Campbell Foundation, the Robert

W. Woodruff Foundation, and the James B. Whitehead Foundation made the difference at critical moments as we rebuilt the zoo. The first $4 million corporate fund-raising campaign was led by Robert Strickland, CEO of Trust Company Bank. Our success with local and national media was due to sage advice and counsel from corporate leaders John Mellot, Gary Nielson, Tom Boyle, Grant Curtis, Andy Fisher, Ken Hollander, Joe Ledlie, Jay Smith, and the talent of Chris Curle, Don Farmer, Virginia Gunn, Stefanie Powers, and Bert Rudman. Martin Gatins was a stalwart resource for fund-raising in the Atlanta corporate community. I thank him for taking me under his wing. Our brilliant marketing director, Gail Eaton, coordinated all of the media players in a dynamic universe of compelling market themes. What started as a local story quickly went viral and appeared in media worldwide, turning Willie B. into the most famous gorilla in the world.

For their creativity and team approach in designing and building the game-changing Ford African Rain Forest exhibit, I thank Mack Taylor, Larry Gellarstadt, Oscar Harris, Chip Robert, Larry Lord, Terry Sargeant, Jon Coe, Gary Lee, Nevin Lash, Harvey Cheatham, Jimmy Wren, Craig Piper, Trish Vecchio, Don Jackson, Gail Bruner, and the hardworking employees at Taylor and Mathis, Beers, and Holder Construction.

In the final analysis, the Association of Zoos and Aquariums (AZA) was a harsh judge, but we passed their tests with flying colors. My hardworking staff deserves all of the credit for achieving and sustaining membership and accreditation while taking the zoo from worst to first. The demands of Bob Wagner and Syd Butler at AZA fueled our long-term commitment to excellence.

For six years of continuous funding, I am grateful to an anonymous donor with a keen interest in wildlife conservation and animal welfare. Without her involvement, my talented wellness team at the Jacksonville Zoo would not exist. Her support has enabled me to continue writing, mentoring, and speaking up for wildlife. For their enthusiastic endorsement of my work in Jacksonville, I thank Tony Vecchio, Dan Maloney, John Lukas, and the board of directors of the Jacksonville Zoo & Gardens.

Operating a research program for such a long period of time requires a cadre of dedicated students and colleagues. They are too numerous to list here, but you'll find them all in the reference section. For their essential role in partership with the University of North Florida, I thank Fatima Ramis, Valerie Segura, Dean George Rainbolt, Les Gasparov, and fellow faculty Michael Toglia, Lori Lange, Cliff Ross, Adam Rosenblatt, and Greg Kohn. The production of this book was achieved by collaboration among talented editors at Palmetto and Red Leaf Press. I thank Chisato Abe, who allowed me to use her beautiful painting of Willie B. on the cover. For the use of his photographs and insight into the behavior of wild mountain gorillas, I thank my friend John Fowler. The specialists at Acer Rubrum assisted in website construction. I thank my daughters Sally Fox Maple and Molly Maple Bryant for generating social media and for other marketing support.

Finally, local government let go of the zoo in 1985, giving the new management team unprecented freedom to change it. We could not have liberated Willie B. without the enthusiastic endorsement of city and county leaders. Our entrepreneurial approach to building a zoo has now been emulated by a nation of other zoos, and they have all enjoyed the same degree of success we have. It is a blessing that, at long last, we could find unity in the daunting task of freeing Willie B.

Terry L. Maple, PhD
Fernandina Beach, FLorida

FIGURE 1-1. WILLIE B. IN SOLITARY CONFINEMENT IN ATLANTA (T. L. MAPLE).

Chapter 1

THE LONG ROAD TO REFORM
AND RENEWAL

My first good look at the magnificent lowland gorilla Willie B. was the highlight of my first day in Atlanta in September 1975. He was the second gorilla to be named after Atlanta's long-time Mayor William B. Hartsfield. The first Willie B. arrived in 1959 and succumbed to viral pneumonia less than two years later. The second Willie B. fared better. The little gorilla created quite a buzz, and local newspaper accounts immediately designated him the zoo's most popular resident. His age was estimated to be 2-1/2 years when he was captured in Cameroon, West Africa, by Deets Pickett, a Kansas City veterinarian and animal dealer. He weighed sixty-five pounds when he arrived at the zoo on May 6, 1961. The city paid $5,500 to acquire him (Reynolds, 2000). Given the impact of his life, this must be regarded as an incredible bargain.

My first impressions of the zoo in 1975 were disturbing. A small zoo, with primates and felines confined to indoor cages, most of the species exhibited were housed in dyads. Willie B. lived alone in isolation from his own kind. The tiny cages were tile and concrete separated from the public by glass barriers or steel bars. Lacking manipulable objects, the barren cages were noisy. In the feline house, strong odor predominated. There was no hint of naturalism, the animals lived in prisons with nothing to do.

Lowland gorillas were at one time an oddity in American zoos and the objects of great public fascination and curiosity. For a small, under-achieving zoo, the acquisition of a gorilla was a remarkable achievement. Willie B.'s special relationship to the mayor meant that he also had value during Hartsfield's many political campaigns. As Hartsfield's namesake, he was more mascot than zoological specimen. In a bizarre political stunt, the first Willie B. actually appeared on the ballot for a seat in Congress. Fortunately, zoos now recognize that gorilla commerce is an unscrupulous practice and no longer trade, purchase, or sell them. Nor do they promote them for public office. All zoo directors are aware of the brutal practices that surrounded the capture of living gorillas and the violent cruelty to others. Silverbacks fiercely resisted capture and often died defending the group. Babies that survived this carnage were stolen from the jungle and taken hostage to exhibit in museums, circuses, and zoos. We look back on this epoch with shame.

THE PLIGHT THICKENS

After a long drive from our home in Davis, California, across the country to the southeastern state of Georgia, my wife Addie and I were eagerly entering the first chapter of my academic career in 1975. I awakened early after a night in a boutique hotel near Emory University and immediately drove to the zoo. It was more important for me to touch base with zoo director Steve Dobbs than it was to claim my new office in the psychology department at Emory. There was a large group of seven Sumatran orangutans housed at the zoo on loan from the Yerkes Primate Center, and I was ready to begin my research on this species.

Mr. Dobbs, a herpetologist by training, informed me that Dr. Richard K. Davenport had arranged for the exhibit so he could continue his investigation into the social proclivities of orangutans. Davenport was an esteemed professor at Georgia Tech and was long affiliated with the Yerkes Primate Center. He had conducted research in Sabah, one of the first field studies of orangutans (Davenport, 1967). Although there was evidence that orangutans were largely solitary, Professor Davenport suspected their social potential had been underestimated, hence his decision to establish a small group of seven animals.

Because Davenport's busy technician spent so little time at the zoo, he agreed that my students and I could use this opportunity to gather additional data and photo-document our work. I greatly valued the collaboration as Davenport had much to teach me. From this moment forward, orangutans were my first research priority. My students and I gathered enough data to publish many important research papers, a book, and several book chapters that began to elevate the profile of this neglected species and the emerging research capabilities of the zoo itself (Maple and Zucker, 1978; Maple et al., 1979; Zucker et al, 1978). Dobbs and crocodile expert Howard Hunt had published before, so they readily accepted collaborators from the nearby universities.

As a subject for our studies, Willie B. might have been a mere afterthought had I not recruited a West Coast graduate student to join me in Atlanta. Mike Hoff arrived in 1976, and we quickly went to work on a collaborative study of gorilla social development with Dr. Ronald D. Nadler. Mike gathered data on the first three lowland gorillas born at the Yerkes National Primate Research Center. The infants and their mothers were maintained in a social group put together at the Yerkes Field Station in Lawrenceville, Georgia. The silverback male, Rann, was the patriarch of this research group. Zoos with gorillas rarely bred them in those days, and if they did produce offspring, they were usually removed for hand-rearing by a human caregiver. Our work with Dr. Nadler resulted in many benchmark publications (Hoff et al., 1981; Hoff et al., 1982; Hoff et al., 1994; Hoff et al., 1996). Based on these early studies and our familiarity with the literature, Mike and I wrote our reference book *Gorilla Behavior* (Maple and Hoff, 1982).

CONNECTING THE DOTS

My first graduate student at Emory, Evan Zucker, had already committed to the orangutan project so, in the spirit of partnership, he and Mike made it possible to see our research in a comparative perspective. Because Willie B. was exhibited as a solitary gorilla, we didn't immediately take an interest in him. Still, I spent enough time at the primate house to begin to appreciate Willie's unique personality while gaining respect for his impact on visitors, volunteers, and staff. He was revered in Atlanta and well-known throughout the South. As the zoo's fortunes waxed and waned over the next two decades, Willie B. became the symbol of the zoo's decline and eventual renewal.

At our first introduction, he was estimated to be sixteen years old, and I was thirty. I weighed 240 pounds, my hair was dark and long, and my beard was in full bloom. Essentially, it seemed as if the gorilla and I occupied the same amount of space. I always thought he regarded me as a competitor, a fellow ape engaged in a quest to elevate our stature. Willie was already becoming a silverback, and I was trying to become one. Neither one of us was yet a proven breeder, but we both understood there could be only one silverback in the room. Whenever he saw me in the primate building, he stiffened and threatened me in the stance reserved for confrontations with rivals. He reacted this way throughout the time we knew each other, even after I did so much to transform his living space into the Garden of Eden that became his new home. Of course, he couldn't possibly know who was responsible for his good fortune. If he tried to thank us, he would have to thank the entire community of good-hearted human beings who cared enough to provide their love and their money. It took a village, a very large one at that, to rise to the occasion and rescue Willie B.

When I returned to our hotel on that first day in Atlanta, I confessed to my wife that the zoo was in bad shape, but I thought I could help. The primate house was especially inhumane. I felt bad for the kids who had to see Willie B. in such deplorable conditions. Having spent my childhood in San Diego, I was inspired and educated by field trips to the world-famous San Diego Zoo. I never felt sorry for the animals living in habitats where they could see blue skies and feel the warmth of the sun. Better yet, gorillas in San Diego lived in social groups. They played, courted, and reproduced with their companions. I didn't realize that these early impressions would influence the direction of my career, but they clearly did.

Intuitively, I knew that an upgraded zoo could do a lot of good for the children of Georgia who would rediscover the joy and wonder of naturalistic simulations of African habitat. From its origins, the San Diego Zoo had been dedicated to educating and inspiring the children of San Diego. That noble purpose shaped its vision and its strategy to become the world's finest zoological park. Like San Diego, the Atlanta Zoo served as a destination for local schoolchildren on educational field trips, but the poor quality of its facilities diminished its value.

As I reflected on the conditions that prevailed at the zoo, I realized that the proximity of Yerkes Primate Center and the potential partnerships with nearby universities and three veterinary schools would be the keys to its survival. It occurred to me even then that the translocation of monkeys and apes from the primate center to the zoo would be good for everyone involved. To achieve this, however, I would have to be successful in making the case to stakeholders in the community and at Emory University. It would take a significant financial investment to see this vision through to the end, but I was already committed to a project that would consume the rest of my life and career.

Years later, no one envied me when I stepped in as interim director to take responsibility for a zoo rated by the Humane Society (HSUS) as one of the nation's worst, but I was confident that reform was feasible, and I expected to be successful from the outset of my journey. I understood that it was unethical to exhibit a solitary gorilla without a plan to socialize the animal, and it would soon become an accreditation issue if we didn't rectify the problem.

Because there were fewer and fewer of these singletons, I did manage to send one of my students up to Philadelphia to make some preliminary observations on the old male, Massa. I thought we could compare him to Willie B. to see how aging had affected him. As Mollie Bloomsmith discovered, Massa looked old, but he didn't seem to be suffering from any behavioral deficits. He moved around less than Willie B., who was half his age, but he actually seemed quite healthy in his fifties. My guess is that he had some cognitive deficits, but no one had evaluated him. This was a missed opportunity in Philadelphia. In fact, isolated apes were common in those days, but they were rarely studied by psychologists.

In addition to his duties at Yerkes, Dr. Geoffrey Bourne was president of the local zoological society. He asked me to join the zoo board in 1976. This put me in direct contact with a dedicated cadre of Atlanta citizens who desperately wanted to change the zoo's direction. They knew then that it would take a removal from city governance to establish a legitimate nonprofit zoological society capable of running a first-class zoo. However, my new friends on the board never expected such intractable resistance from the city. It took a scandalous series of management errors in the late seventies and early eighties to shake the confidence of city fathers and enlist the help of private sector leaders. I became involved at a time when reform seemed possible.

In 1978, after the sudden death of Professor Davenport at the young age of fifty, I was recruited to replace him at Georgia Tech. It was bittersweet, but the move from Emory to Tech was just the tonic that I needed. The director of Tech's School of Psychology, Dr. Edward Loveland, offered me a promotion to associate professor after just three years at Emory and significantly improved my salary. Such a rapid advance was unusual in academia, so it was an offer I could not refuse. Soon after I joined the Tech faculty, my first book, *Orang-utan Behavior,* was published by Van Nostrand Reinhold Company (Maple, 1980). This book was the first of a package I promised to deliver, one book each on chimpanzees, gorillas, and orangutans. I was happy with the gorilla and orangutan books, but I never finished the book on chimpanzees. At least not yet. There is so much written material about chimpanzees that it will require another lifetime to get it done. I happily pass the baton to one of my many former graduate students. Following the model of my two previous books with Van Nostrand, a comprehensive chimpanzee book for the enlightenment of zoo professionals is long overdue.

MENTORING MAPLE

In 1980, after two years at Tech, I accepted an invitation from the innovative young zoo director Ron Forman to serve as interim general curator in

New Orleans on a nine-month sabbatical at the Audubon Zoo. With the encouragement of my colleagues at Tech, it was a dynamic setting where I could learn more about how modern zoos were actually run. Ron was in the midst of his own revolutionary transformation of a decrepit city zoo, and it was a good time to observe the process of change firsthand. Meanwhile, Atlanta's crisis just kept deepening, and the media's investigative reporters were energetically exposing every flaw. When I returned to Atlanta in September 1981, the zoo had reached rock bottom, and I began to wonder if city fathers would ever turn to me for help. Forman taught me the importance of private sector support for a struggling city zoo. Eventually, city fathers in New Orleans gave him what he wanted; greater autonomy for entrepreneurial management. I knew this approach could be replicated in Atlanta. The key ingredient, of course, was leadership and Ron Forman was the right leader at the right time in New Orleans.

After a particularly bad series of media stories in 1983, I finally received a Friday afternoon call from Mayor Andrew Young's office, asking me to meet with him on Monday morning to discuss the zoo crisis. Among a small group of fellow experts, we met with the Mayor and Commissioner Carolyn Boyd Hatcher for an hour. It was clear to me that Mayor Young didn't know much about the unique requirements of a modern zoo, but it was painful for him to see animals and citizens suffering in our city. He could see that what zoo management was doing was not working. I recall his simplified conclusion that the reptile folks didn't seem to like the mammal folks and vice versa. He was right about that, but it wasn't the whole story. The group agreed that the zoo was hopelessly divided and needed to rally behind a uniform command.

By the end of our hour with Mayor Young, the group concluded that only immediate and strong leadership would alter the course of our zoo. The discussion soon turned to candidates who were qualified and available for this task. Somehow the group reached the conclusion that I should consider becoming the new zoo director. The idea made sense, but I could not agree to the suggestion immediately, as I needed a private meeting with Commissioner Hatcher to nail down the details and outline my requirements for such a challenging assignment. I also needed approval from officials at Georgia Tech, so my answer would have to be delayed a few days. Mrs. Hatcher ended the meeting by cautioning the group to keep this decision confidential until she and I and the mayor could finalize it.

By the time I had driven the fifteen minutes from City Hall to my office at Tech, reporters were already camped outside my office. They pointed microphones at my face and asked me if I was going to be the new zoo director. I could not believe that one of my trusted colleagues had already leaked the story. I called Carolyn and complained that the media had entrapped me and that I was on the verge of telling my first lie. Had I denied it, my credibility would have been compromised.

That night Addie and I watched the talking heads speculate about my fate. A few days later my contract with the zoo was confirmed. It wasn't a simple transaction because the city had to go to step seven of its graduated pay scale to match my modest academic salary at Tech. In those days, City of Atlanta government would not pay a competitive salary to its zoo director. It may have been an example of passive aggression, their way of forcing Steve Dobbs to give up and resign. Certainly, our city fathers did not regard the zoo as a high priority for funding. Although vastly undercompensated, Steve liked his job and wouldn't be intimidated. Eventually, the city and Mr. Dobbs agreed on a retirement package, but the crisis deepened with no leader at the helm. Any student of primatology could have predicted this outcome. When the leader falters, chaos always ensues.

I was hired to stop the bleeding, and I agreed to serve three months until the start of classes in September. I took over on June 15, 1984. I never intended to stay long, and no one expected me to, but circumstances improved almost immediately. A privatization plan was approved by government and civic leaders later that year, and the new board leaders offered me the position of President/CEO of the new nonprofit, Zoo Atlanta (aka Atlanta/Fulton County Zoo). My reform administration gained traction immediately, and I was extended for another year, and then another, until I had served eighteen years of consecutive one-year verbal contracts. I've always believed that the growing public confidence was due to my academic credentials. People didn't know me, but they liked the fact that a Georgia Tech professor was in charge.

TRANSITIONS

I didn't immediately love my job due to the high stress compared to my life as a college professor, but it was an easy transition for me to express my innate leadership genes. I discovered long ago that leading was in my blood, and my teachers and coaches along the way nurtured my skills as I began to practice leadership in my youth. In spite of my success, it was humiliating to endure the hostile scrutiny of the media, who constantly pursued me at the zoo and at home. I changed my phone number to protect my wife from one particularly vicious reporter. It was necessary to separate myself and my key staff from the zoo's long, dysfunctional history and to craft a new identity as the team that would provide the solutions to long-standing problems. In the early days of my administration, I had to dodge media bullets aimed at city government and anyone who worked for them. I was a new face with big ideas, but I would have to prove myself.

One investigative reporter at the *Atlanta Journal-Constitution*, Susan Faludi, was particularly troublesome because she had a direct pipeline to disgruntled zookeepers. They were not immediately convinced that I was on their side, so they continued to feed her misinformation to sabotage my leadership. After one egregious newspaper article that embarrassed my newly recruited middle managers, I was persuaded to respond with a lengthy rebuttal. To my surprise, the editors printed my entire letter along with a flattering photograph. Ms. Faludi, who later won a Pulitzer Prize for her book *The Glass Ceiling* (1991), never wrote another story about the zoo. Perhaps she thought her last article was a fitting end to her exposure of the zoo's deficiencies as she left Atlanta to compete on a bigger stage. Better yet, it appeared the newspaper had kicked my tires long enough to begin believing in the new leadership team.

For the remainder of my career at the zoo, we received positive publicity. The *AJC* and all other media outlets in the city began to tell the story of Zoo Atlanta's revitalization process. On television, the zoo was no longer the lead that was bleeding. Instead, it became the happy story that lifted spirits each and every evening they covered us. The reader can learn more about this transitional period of the zoo's history in a comprehensive account published by the *Journal of the Atlanta History Society* (Desiderio, 2000). I've also revealed some of these historical details in my books *Zoo Man* (1995), *Saving the Giant Panda* (2000), and *Professor in the Zoo* (Maple, 2016). Two chapters written for the book *Ethics on the Ark* (1993) are particularly relevant reading to understand the whole story of our revitalization and recovery and our new focus on conservation.

The most unique feature of our privatization is the fact that it was and still is a collaboration between government, the corporate community, and academia. As different as these sectors can be, we had no difficulty in building a strong coalition. For example, in the early days when the City of Atlanta operated the zoo, the Atlanta Zoological Society (AZS) was established as a successor nonprofit operator should the city choose to get out of the zoo business. In 1970, prominent academicians Goeffrey Bourne and Duane Rumbaugh worked with Atlanta attorney Richard Reynolds to produce the first bylaws for a scientific zoological society in Atlanta. They saw the future of zoos from the lens of their leadership experience at Yerkes and the noble history of the San Diego Zoological Society.

As it turned out, in spite of their heavy lifting during years of crisis, the zoological society never inherited the zoo, but it played a supporting role when a new, nonprofit board was appointed in 1985. The new board was comprised of seven distinguished corporate leaders and two former officers of the AZS board. The new zoo board was unique in its composition: racially and gender balanced to reflect the diversity of Atlanta. Each member was vetted by Bob Petty, chairman of the zoological society, and Parks Commissioner Carolyn Hatcher and was approved by Mayor Young and Marvin Arrington, chairman of the Atlanta-Fulton County Recreation Authority (AFCRA). The legal mechanism to change governance from the city to a new nonprofit was the brainchild of Mr. Arrington, who did as much as any local politician to rescue the zoo. The new board was a serious upgrade to our ability to influence public and private support for the zoo. Once the priorities of our community were realigned, government had set the table for a new dynamic leader.

The zoo was now a public/private partnership—run like a nonprofit, but connected to government through AFCRA. We were very fortunate that one of the most dynamic corporate leaders in the city, Bob Holder, agreed to serve as our first chairman. He gave us four years of strong leadership, more than any other chairman in zoo history. An oil painting of Mr. Holder hangs in the zoo administration building to acknowledge his impact. Arrington's plan produced the first $16 million of government funding to jump-start design and construction of the new zoo.

It pleased me that the founding visionaries and the entire board of the zoological society were present when we opened the Ford African Rain Forest, and Willie B. entered the outdoors for the first time since he was violently kidnapped from his forest home. The happiest witnesses to this great event were those who worked so hard for reform during the eighteen years of its transformation to nonprofit management. Although I knew many of them individually, many others were to me a kind of anonymous flock of men and women dedicated to change. They now have pride of ownership and should feel good about achieving victory. The new board made it happen, but many other volunteers kept the momentum going in the toughest times. The credit was widely shared, and the entire city took a bow that night.

A LITTLE BEAR GOES WEST

During my first year on the job, I faced some difficult decisions. I was unprepared for irrational management on my watch, but I had to deal with it. Our baby polar bear Andy was named for Mayor Young, and he was very popular. I knew that we could not adequately care for him, so I looked for an opportunity to loan him to another zoo with a better polar bear facility in a more favorable climate. I had no reason to doubt the sex of this bear, but it turned out that he was actually a female. The staff perpetrated this falsehood to prevent the animal from being moved to another zoo. Our keepers treated him well, but they regarded Andy as more of a pet than a zoo animal. I saw it differently. Not yet knowing Andy bear's true gender, I made a deal with the San Francisco Zoo to send him to the West Coast for breeding purposes. As it is with gorillas, zoo experts took a dim view of singleton bear exhibits, and our decrepit facilities did not do justice to this cute little bear. It took time for the San Francisco veterinarians to discover he was actually a female, much to my embarrassment. To move this popular bear, I had to go directly to the mayor to get his blessing. He readily agreed that whatever was good for the bear was good for Atlanta. This was the vote of confidence that I needed from City Hall. I had to solve a lot of pesky problems like this on my way to the more challenging issues of reimagining a new zoo.

VISIONARY PLANNING AND DESIGN

Zoo designers such as Jones & Jones and Coe & Lee strongly advocated landscape immersion to benefit the animals and the people who paid good money to see them. It was a big idea to upgrade the facilities for all of the gorillas we hoped to acquire. If we could strike a deal with Yerkes Primate Center, we would have the opportunity to build one of the largest facilities for gorillas ever attempted. As we were planning our gorilla exhibit, I had to answer tough questions about the future of Willie B. Could he be safely introduced to other gorillas? Did he have a future as a solitary silverback, or should we try to socialize him? This was a moment in AZA history when male gorillas were routinely moved from one zoo to another to diversify the gene pool or to improve their welfare. At one point, I speculated that if the AZA gorilla committee asked me to move him to another zoo, I would have to seriously consider it. Willie B. had not yet bred, so his genes were not yet represented in the managed AZA population. Objectively, his genes were more important to the AZA than he was. Fortunately, the request never came, and I never had to face up to that problem.

In spite of our success in rehabilitating Willie B., if they had had to choose, I honestly believe that Atlanta citizens would have preferred to trade *me* to another zoo to keep Willie B. in our city. Who knows how this story would have ended had we moved him in 1984? Zoo directors are supposed to have the final say in animal management decisions, but moving an animal with the stature of Willie B. would require a higher authority.

In a city whose corporate history is dominated by Coca-Cola, I once had the heretical thought of building a polar bear exhibit sponsored by their hated competitor, Pepsi-Cola. Coca-Cola marketing executives hit a home run with their animated polar bear commercials, and I thought they owed a debt of gratitude to the bears and our long-suffering zoo. I still believe that Pepsi would have jumped at the chance to build a major polar bear exhibit in the home town of their rival. Only an egregious offense of this magnitude would compare to how I would have been treated had Willie B. left us for another city.

One way or another, I knew that Willie B. was fated to meet other zoo gorillas, so we would have to acquire them ourselves. At this point in time, Willie B. was bigger than the zoo itself. And we were still waiting for our friends at Coca-Cola to sponsor a world-class exhibit for polar bears at Zoo Atlanta. Fortunately, Coke was generous in other ways. Their significant gift provided the resources to design and build the Coca-Cola World Studio, a highly innovative lecture and media room with ample seating for schoolchildren and world-class acoustics. And years later, as we negotiated with China, the company produced an animated commercial with giant pandas promoting their product. Unfortunately, Chinese audiences didn't like the commercial, so the company never released it.

We knew that the Yerkes gorillas were a gold mine of opportunity for behavioral studies, and the integration of Willie B., if achievable, would be a benchmark achievement. As we awaited the construction of the new exhibits, we continued our research with orangutans. Our publications and presentations were getting noticed in the late seventies, and we made some important discoveries about the species. For example, we were the first scientists to document adult orangutan paternal behavior (Zucker, Mitchell, and Maple, 1978), and the brilliant 1976 honors thesis of undergraduate honors student Mary Beth Dennon led to the discovery of female proceptivity in orangs (Maple, Zucker, and Dennon, 1979). Earlier research documented this phenomenon in gorillas and chimpanzees but not orangutans, when cycling females approached males to initiate copulation. We documented on film repeated episodes of proceptivity in one pair of animals that Beth observed for ninety days. Our published findings put our Emory

University lab on the map, and the results were confirmed experimentally by R. D. Nadler at Yerkes (1977). Our collaboration with Dr. Nadler was bearing intellectual fruit.

Georgia Tech administrators recognized opportunity in my appointment at the zoo, so I was encouraged to blend both of my careers. As the entrepreneurial CEO, I implemented a scientific program with an applied emphasis, and my cadre of highly motivated students were able to develop viable doctoral dissertations from the work they conducted under my supervision. Over the years, twenty-seven students completed master's and PhD degrees at the zoo. Most of them were women. I wrote about the advance of women in zoo biology in an article published recently (Maple, 2021). They were recruited from a perspective known in psychology as the "scientist-practitioner" model, since so many of my students ended up working with management responsibilities in the zoo world. Their combination of scientific and management experience made them ideal targets for outside recruitment. Because I had been assigned the task of reforming the zoo, it became a *tabula rasa* for the board of directors and for my employees and students. Together we accomplished what seemed in the beginning to be an impossible assignment (see Maple, 2019; Hoff et al., 2014). We were all neophytes at reconstructing a zoo, but we found a way to do it while simultaneously studying the effects of our reforms. The zoos that hired my students were getting tested employees who were baptized in the fire of intense media scrutiny. They never flinched.

THE CUPBOARD WAS BARE

So, what was wrong with the Atlanta Zoo when I took the helm in 1984? First, the puny zoo budget of $622,201 in 1978 was woefully inadequate, and there was little hope that funding would improve. The facilities were dilapidated, and animals were clearly suffering. City administrators and leaders of the Atlanta Zoological Society did not have confidence in the zoo's management team. As a result, the zoo director had no power to get anything done. Mr. Dobbs' plight was openly debated in the local media.

A 1978 article by Michelle Green in the *Atlanta Journal-Constitution* observed that zoo staff blamed the society for fostering ill will and paranoia by working against the embattled director. Floating in financial limbo, lacking a strategic plan, the zoo continued to drift from mediocrity to a state of crisis management. Eventually, Dobbs left his post, and soon thereafter disputes and character assassination ruled the day. Psychologists call this state "diffusion of responsibility," as no one was in charge. The zoo was in chaos, but I never blamed Steve Dobbs. In my opinion, he was treated unfairly and never given the support he needed to succeed. After his departure, locked in a power vacuum, the zoo was not better off without him.

Commissioner Hatcher heroically tried to resuscitate the zoo, but her invitation to AZA authorities for an inspection did not turn out well. A visiting committee found evidence of mismanagement and neglect. One of the inspectors, Satch Krantz, stated in an interview with local media: "I have seen things in the Atlanta zoo that I have never seen in 12 years as a zoo professional." AZA's full report went on to conclude, "Never have we encountered such an environment of mistrust, anger and doubt among the top levels of management in any zoo." In Atlanta and beyond, the animal rights community was well aware of the zoo's problems, and they demanded reforms. The board of AZA was so disappointed in the state of the zoo they elected to remove the city's credentials as a member of the association. This bold step was unprecedented in the history of AZA.

When I was appointed interim director in 1984, AZA executive Bob Wagner told me that the Atlanta Zoo had embarrassed its peers and faced strong opposition to reinstatement. They were angry that the attention of media had been turned on them as communities began to ask questions about the state of their own local zoological facilities. On the day that Mayor Young introduced me, the room was packed with local, regional, and national investigative reporters. He urged me to speak candidly and not back down. The mayor reminded me that reporters had once hounded him to resign his position at the United Nations, and he vowed not to ever let that happen again. He assured me the city was committed to repairing the zoo brick by brick. When a reporter asked me if my hands would be tied by the city, I lifted my arms and grumbled, "See these two fists!" A bit of comic relief, this was my way of reducing the tension. Even though it was clear that the road to reconciliation would be painful and long, I had a fighting chance to succeed.

ASPIRING TO GREATNESS

One of the first principles I articulated as the new leader was simple. At 35 acres, Zoo Atlanta was modest in size, but we didn't have to be big to be great; we only had to be great. These aspirations were reflected in the quality of our current and future employees, volunteers, and academic collaborators. In our case, being great meant being smart. From the early days of my administration, I concentrated on hiring the smartest people I could find in the marketplace. All of my business mentors, including Ford executives, agreed that our stature was not limited by our size. Ford was, after all, the number two automaker in numbers, but they built the best cars. I was hired to stop the bleeding, but I refused to put a band-aid on our problems. More permanent intervention was needed. As we planned our future, we set our sights on becoming the "world's next great zoo." Fortunately, city fathers and the new zoo board let me take the zoo in a bold new direction.

Dr. Maple and zoo miracles

T he trickle of good news from the Atlanta Zoo continues. Not quite a year since primatologist Terry Maple took over as director, gorilla Willie B. has been adopted by the Kiwanis Club of Northside Atlanta, which gave $1,000 toward zoo maintenance, and an Atlanta family has donated $50,000 toward a planned "Great Ape" exhibit.

It's true that Maple didn't have to do much to make the old crowd look bad. But the current level of confidence in the zoo is an indication that Maple is much more than merely adequate. Congratulations, Maple. The zoo needed you.

FIGURE 1-2. EARLY EDITORIAL FROM THE *ATLANTA JOURNAL-CONSTITUTION*.

The rebranded and privatized Zoo Atlanta rose to become an institutional leader in the zoo profession, and my affiliated research lab documented the change by publishing more than 250 papers and books on primate exhibition, management, and the emerging subject of zoo biology. No zoo has ever documented its recovery to the extent we did. Looking back on all that we achieved, it is comforting to know that we have told much of the story, but there is so much left to tell. This is why I decided to write a biographical account of Atlanta's iconic ape. His story is a metaphor for an institutional transformation like no other. Because Zoo Atlanta became a model for other zoos, it is a story that resonates with other zoo leaders, and I had a front row seat for most of his adult life at the zoo until his death in 2000 at the estimated age of forty-one.

I observed Willie B., formally and informally, for twenty-five years. I feel comfortable telling his story as a generation of Atlanta citizens have reached adulthood unaware of the life and legacy of this charismatic primate. There are others who knew him well enough to write this book. Dr. Rita McManamon, our veterinarian, arrived at the zoo in 1984, and she tended to him until the end of his life. She conducted his annual physical, tended to his aches and pains, and brought in the best doctors to treat him when his ailments were serious. But the person who knew him best, Charles Horton, knew him in a different way than I did. Charles fed him, played with him, talked to him, and prepared him for bed every day for many years. As the one who brought dignitaries and new friends to meet Willie B., I had the pleasure of seeing how much joy he brought to our community. I also made the key decisions to rehabilitate and re-socialize him through diligent fund-raising and by convening creative architects and scientists who helped to design his future. So, as much as this book is about Willie B., it is also the story of a community unified by the urgent need to upgrade an institution, and the roles we all played in liberating him. Because of the vast numbers of local, regional, and national supporters who played a part in this drama, I will never be able to properly acknowledge them. But you, dear reader, were there beside me, and you will always understand what it took to get the job done. Willie B.'s story parallels my own, as we both reached the zenith of our full potential in Atlanta.

Terry L. Maple

Zoo Atlanta is still evolving now that it has been led by two chief executives beyond my time at the helm. They each transformed the zoo to continue its commitment to excellence. When I first became director, I dreamed of the day when the zoo would be good enough to attract the highest-qualified candidates to succeed me. Thankfully, that day came when the zoo hired Dennis Kelly, who still resides in the city in his position as dean of the Hammack School of Business at Oglethorpe University. To his credit, Dennis kept me informed as he made changes in the organization. The innovative Great Ape Heart Project, led by Dr. Hayley Murphy, has flourished with the support of current CEO Raymond King. His expertise at fund-raising resulted in a new African savannah exhibit with unique public viewing of giraffe, elephants, and rhinos. Thanks to both of these men, Atlanta's pre-eminence in gorilla biology and behavior is still unchallenged.

I've been honored to spend quality time in the company of many famous apes over the years, but Willie B. is by far the most fascinating primate I ever met. I left my post at the zoo in 2003 and retired from Georgia Tech in 2008, so the time is right for me to share what I know about Willie B.'s remarkable life. I hope the readers will find his story as inspiring as it was for me to write about it. His life is meant to be enjoyed and celebrated. With the arrival of giant pandas in December 1999, it was as if Willie B. purposely passed the torch to the newest superstars of the zoo world. As wonderful as they are, they will never replace Willie B.

After he passed away, we decided to identify a sculptor who was assigned the task of depicting Willie B. for the appreciation of future generations. We hired Edwin Bogucki, who executed Wille B.'s image perfectly. The life-size bronze statue can be approached for photographs while old-timers tell stories to eager children and grandchildren who only know him by the still-vivid memories of kinfolk. His cremated remains were placed within the sculpture and dedicated on April 20, 2001. In this form, we believe Willie B. will live forever in the hearts and minds of Atlanta's citizens and the other friends he made around the world. My interest in great apes stoked my own desire to become a father. Our three children, Molly, Emily, and Sally, grew up with Willie B., and our memory of this unique

18

and sentient being continues to motivate us to achieve harmony in our own lives.

FIGURE 1-3. TERRY AND WILLIE B. (A. G. MAPLE).

Atlanta's advance as a leading southern city reflected the growth and maturity of the silverback whose life blossomed when our community chose to elevate the priority of his cause.

Chapter 2

THE RELENTLESS PURSUIT
OF WILD GORILLAS

FIGURE 2-1. GORILLA HUNTING EXPEDITIONS WERE BRUTAL.

At the turn of the twentieth century, explorers and collectors arrived in Africa to acquire specimens for the great museums of Europe and North America. Teddy Roosevelt led an expedition to Africa in 1909 representing the Smithsonian Institute. He shot 296 animals and collected their pelts, feathers, and usable parts for museum curators. Gorillas were not so easy to obtain dead or alive. The massive animals resisted capture so fiercly that entire families were slaughtered to supply pelts, skeletons, and appendages for taxidermy and to bring back baby animals for exhibition. Gorilla hunts were publicized in newspapers and books written by the explorers and their biographers. All of these expeditions were bloody, cruel, and wasteful efforts, but the public was fascinated by gorillas. In 1915, representing the New York Zoological Society (now the Wildlilfe Conservation Society), William T. Hornaday commented on the challenge of capturing adult gorillas in his paper "Gorillas, Past and Present":

> There is not the slightest reason to hope that an adult gorilla, either male or female, ever will be seen living in a zoological park or garden. Large speciments cannot be caught alive . . . the savage and implacable nature of the animal is against it.

Hornaday's pessimism didn't discourage gorilla hunters from trying, and many young gorillas suffered the fate of capture and delivery from Africa to their distant destinations. In a white paper dated June 15, 2000, Atlanta attorney Richard Reynolds, Zoo Atlanta's official historian, described the arduous journey of infant gorillas captured in Africa at the turn of the century:

> There was grueling travel, first by porterage, then a long journey at sea to Europe followed by another to America. If the zoo were inland, there was a further ride by train. Throughout, the little animals were constantly exposed to human bacteriological and viral infections to which they were terribly susceptible. Faced with all that, most were near goners when they arrived at the final destination.

The lowland species was the more accessible taxon when explorers such as Paul Du Chaillus pursued them to bring back specimens for placement in the world's great museums. One of the most impressive collections of African field artifacts and taxidermy is housed in Antwerp, Belgium, an impressive record of the nation's imperialistic history in Congo.

FIGURE 2-2. A MOUNTAIN GORILLA FAMILY IN RWANDA (J. D. FOWLER).

Chicago's Field Museum and the American Museum of Natural History in New York housed exhibits of gorilla groups put together by Carl Akeley. Akeley (1923) later became an advocate for gorilla conservation, and he was instrumental in setting up the first protected national park in the Belgian Congo. Early in his pursuit of his first wild gorilla, he made the following insightful observation about them:

> I believe that the gorilla is normally a perfectly amiable and decent creature. I believe that if he attacks man it is because he is being attacked or thinks that he is being attacked. I believe that he will fight in self-defense and probably in defense of his family; that he will keep away from a fight until he is frightened or driven into it. (Akeley, 1920, p. 165).

Many books were written by American and European explorers that described humanity's pursuit of gorillas, including Ben Burbridge's classic *Gorilla: Tracking and Capturing the Ape-Man of Africa*, published in 1928. Mr. Burbridge was a North Florida entrepreneur from Jacksonville who recorded his adventures in Africa, producing documentary material, including film, at a time when little was known about gorillas. He succeeded in bringing home two gorillas, with one of them, Congo, living long enough to attract the attention of Yale comparative psychologist Robert M. Yerkes. At the time, Professor Yerkes was earning a reputation as the world's most accomplished student of primate behavior. His interest in the intellect of apes will be discussed in detail in Chapter 7. For a detailed history of the Akeley expeditions tied to his museum taxidermy, see Kirk (2010).

The reference book written by Yerkes and his wife Ada (Yerkes and Yerkes, 1929) stood for years as the most thorough review of great ape behavior and a good starting point for any new research. In my books, I reviewed all that was known about these taxa since the Yerkes' book was published. I examined the literature from both captive and field studies. It has been my pleasure to apply this knowledge by helping to design superior zoo exhibits and most recently an innovative enclosure for bonobos and gorillas at the Jacksonville Zoo and Gardens. In this location, opened in 2019, we have initiated studies of ape cognition with apparatus designed to generate behavioral data and provide enrichment for the animals we test. A highlight of this exhibit is a cognitive workstation located in a specialized, artificial kapok tree known locally as the Wellness Tree.

OTHER APES

Our workstation innovations have prepared Jacksonville to be the latest venue for cognitive studies of apes, following similar zoo facilities in Atlanta and Chicago. The Jacksonville Zoo/University of North Florida research partnership is currently directed by postdoctoral fellow Dr. Lindsay Mahovetz. She previously worked with Frans de Waal. From his base at Emory University, de Waal (de Waal and Lanting, 1997; Pollack and de

Waal, 2007) he directed extensive studies of bonobo mentality, gestures, and sociality. Several colonies exist where other primate psychologists have continued to expand our knowledge of this unique species (e.g., Herrmann, et al., 2010). Common chimpanzees (*P. troglodytes*) are thought to be the ape with the largest repertoire of mental skills, but Yerkes found that gorillas and orang-utans ranked high on all metrics for intellect. However, it took much longer for enough data to be obtained from a critical mass of subjects to properly compare all taxa. We are still gathering these data. Today, many of the apes available for research are exhibited by zoos in naturalistic facilities that promote psychological well-being and wellness (cf. Maple, 2019). Two of the most prolific research facilities focused on great apes are the comparative lab established by Tomasello and Call at the Leipzig Zoo in Germany and the Iowa Great Ape Trust project in Des Moines, Iowa. These projects have been well funded by private and government sources. The future of Leipzig is unclear due to the departure of its founders, but we can hope that it will continue under new direction. Now known as the Ape Cognition and Conservation Initiative, the Iowa facility is lsocated on 230 acres of lowlands, riverine forest, and lakes in southeast Des Moines. It too has experienced changes at the top of the organization. The land was a gift from businessman Ted Townsend, who founded the facility in a collaboration with primatologist Sue Savage-Rumbaugh in 2006. It currently houses six bonobos and is dedicated to increasing our understanding of the biological origins of culture, language, tool use, and intelligence.

The Association of Zoos and Aquariums (AZA), through its Species Survival Plans, have committed resources to cooperatively manage the remaining numbers of bonobos and expand the captive population. This has become a top conservation priority of the AZA and other regional and global conservation organizations such as the European Association of Zoos and Aquariums (EAZA) and the World Association of Zoos and Aquariums (WAZA). Cognitive studies of apes will likely contribute to the strength of our protection programs. Empirical zoos are positioned to study them while simultaneously protecting their native habitats. The captive population should be a model to inspire our best efforts to protect ecosystems where apes evolved.

There is no question that Willie B. kindled empathy in all who visited him in Atlanta. Just as our city was motivated to improve his quality of life, we can hope that revitalized zoological parks will play an important role in conserving wild gorillas and their fragile ecosystems. An example of this fragility is the recent ambush and murder of six park rangers in the Democratic Republic of Congo's Virunga National Park (Reuters, 2021). More than two hundred park rangers have been killed by well-armed poachers in the recent past. Virunga is Africa's oldest national park and its largest tropical rain forest reserve, covering 3,000 square miles. Dian Fossey witnessed illegal captures of infant gorillas in Rwanda for export to European zoos, noting that as many as ten gorillas would be killed defending themselves. In response to these events, Fossey trained her own private patrols to prevent trapping and poaching in her Karisoke study area.

FIGURE 2-3. WILLIE B. IN A FAMILIAR POSE AT THE OLD ZOO (G. CLARKE, AJC, VIA AP).

While the earliest interest in great apes was exploitive and disastrous for the ape population, the one hundred years that followed saw the focus shift from the exhibition of taxidermy in museums to the successful exhibition of live animals to local people. Conservation organizations need to generate support and hope for wild populations and ecosystems. While zoos were once depicted as exploiters of wildlife, superior zoos no longer capture them for exhibition. In fact, we are ultimately dedicated to returning them to currently depleted native habitats, once they can be protected in these restored and revitalized locations. I am optimistic that we can eventually provide sufficient protection for endangered apes in a world troubled by conflict and war. Their survival depends on improving living conditions for the primates that are exhibited in the world's zoos. Substandard exhibits where it is evident that the animals are not living well do not go unnoticed by zoo visitors. If visitors feel sorry for the animals in the zoo, the institution exhibiting them risks a loss of credibility and financial support from the community. When we try to educate our visitors about conservation, substandard exhibits challenge the notion that we can be trusted stewards of wildlife. Effective conservation messaging depends on the quality and the authenticity of our exhibits.

Field and conservation biologists now recognize that animal welfare is an issue in the home ranges of species we are protecting. Poaching is not only fatal, it is brutal, and the animals pursued by poachers suffer. Their suffering is what originally attracted the attention of animal rights and welfare organizations such as the Humane Society of the United States (HSUS). They now monitor animal welfare violations in wild populations. It is unfortunate that organizations such as HSUS and institutions with a lengthy history of protection (Wildlife Conservation Society, World Wildlife Fund) have thus far failed to form effective coalitions to strengthen our efforts. Instead they compete and often overlap in their oversight.

At Zoo Atlanta, as we upgraded facilities such as the Ford African Rain Forest exhibit, we simultaneously committed to investments in field conservation. Dr. Tom Butynski, an experienced conservation biologist and field scientist, was hired to lead our science and conservation program in Africa. Our general curator, Dietrich Schaaf, introduced me to Butynski, who was a perfect fit with our needs in Africa. Tom studied fencing to protect rhinos and elephants from poachers, carried out evaluations for the Kenya Wildlife Service, and wrote several important papers on gorilla conservation. When we connected departments to form our Conservation Action Resource Center at the zoo, we were able to integrate conservation, education, research, and technology. In many zoos, these operating units are siloed. Better communication is achieved with the integrative approach we have taken. For example, the knowledge we gain in the field can be transmitted to our educators and then rapidly shared with our visitors, donors, sponsors, and friends. In this way, a commitment to Willie B.'s quality of life and our zoo's management infrastructure required an equal investment in gorilla protection in Africa. We were able to support Dr. Butynski's position for nine years, but financial constraints forced its discontinuation. I regret that I was unable to set up an endowment for Butynski's unique program. If we could have matched the Smithgall-Watts/Bailey endowments with permanent funding to support our scientific efforts in the field, our impact in conservation would have been multiplied.

Zoos that employ at least one dedicated field scientist are making significant strides in wildlife protection. Jacksonville Zoo and Gardens is invested in Congo, where zoologist John Lukas has operated an Okapi conservation center for many years. John networks with other conservation biologists globally and often puts himself at risk to work in other conservation hot spots. Our philosophy in Jacksonville is similar to the approach my administration took in Atlanta and West Palm Beach. We opened our doors for talks by staff and outside experts, so our community received timely inside information on the world's most challenging conservation issues. These sessions are always well received, and they help us to formulate effective strategies to protect ecosystems and save species.

When I served as CEO of the Palm Beach Zoo, I set up a Conservation Leadership Lecture series sponsored by Florida Crystals Company. In 2005, we were honored to host George Schaller, who reviewed his expeditions to study mountain gorillas, giant pandas, and many of the world's big cats. In Jacksonville, we partnered with the University of North Florida to organize a lecture to celebrate Charles Darwin's birthday. This year's talk was presented by Dr. Billly Karesh of EcoHealth Alliance, a veterinarian who has carried out research on viral agents that threaten to become pandemics, most recently the Covid-19 virus (Karesh, 2005; 2009). Years ago, Billy travelled with me to Sumatra to collect genetic material from wild orangutans. His research helped us to understand the genetic distance of Sumatran and Bornean orangs, a necessary task as we were segregating zoo populations of these two subspecies. These public talks proved to me that education, conservation, and science must be linked. In Atlanta, we periodically summoned Butynski to his home base to brief the troops. His reports from Africa always lifted our spirits and sharpened the focus of our public programs.

AZA zoos and aquariums enjoy the support of visitors, sponsors, and donors. This support is reflected in the financial contributions that AZA institutions have made to conservation programs throughout the world. AZA estimates the association's members have contributed $11 million to gorilla, chimpanzee, orangutan, and bonobo conservation, including rehabilitation, reintroduction, habitat restoration, anti-poaching, and regional monitoring. Both human and financial resources are required to get the job done. It is essential that our institutions promote the good news of our successes and not just the grim decline of species and wild places. We will need optimism and high morale to continue our fight to protect apes and other endangered species. Zoos and aquariums are uniquely positioned to tell the conservation story.

Chapter 3

A NEW PRIMATE IN TOWN

In graduate school, at the University of California at Davis, I trained with Dr. Gary Mitchell, a protege of famed developmental psychologist Dr. Harry F. Harlow. Harlow is therefore my academic grandfather. In Mitchell's lab we studied attachment, parenting, the deleterious effects of social deprivation and isolation, and the remedial effects of socialization in rhesus monkeys and baboons.

FIGURE 3-1. THE AUTHOR WITH A NEWBORN ORANGUTAN IN 1978.

With funding from the Giannini Medical Foundation, and one year as a postdoctoral fellow at the UC Davis medical school in behavioral biology, I was well prepared to join the faculty at Emory University in Atlanta.

Atlanta in 1975 was the perfect place for a young primatologist just beginning his career. Graduate programs in anthropology, biology, and psychology focused on primates in laboratories at Emory, Georgia State, Georgia Tech, and the University of Georgia. All of these institutions were located within a seventy-five-minute drive from the zoo. Esteemed faculty were in place throughout the city, and the population of students created a critical mass for creativity and collaboration. There was no lack of interest or ideas in the Atlanta primate community. Dr. Davenport at Tech and Dr. Duane Rumbaugh at Georgia State had both conducted serious behavioral research in a zoo setting (Maple, 1979a; Maple and Kuhar, 2006).

My own background in developmental psychopathology in primates provided insight into the psychological trauma that Willie B. had suffered when he was violently removed from the arms of his mother. When I was introduced to him, he had been separated from his own kind for seventeen years, and my new colleagues at Emory endlessly debated whether he could ever be socialized and integrated into a normal social group. This was my area of expertise, but even I could not say whether he would recover to express normal social skills after such a long history of isolation. I had no crystal ball, but I was willing to put Willie's social potential to the empirical test. How much social history had he retained from his brief life in a wild group with his mother? We have no record of his life in the wild, but we can reconstruct his early experience from the observations of scientists who have studied gorillas in wild settings. Once he could interact with other gorillas, we were rolling the dice on his future.

Baby gorillas are carried on their mother's bellies and later transfer to their backs. Sometimes they develop idiosyncratic preferences for the mother's arms and legs and hang on for dear life as she locomotes and forages for food. When the group stops to rest, babies begin to explore their surroundings by carefully venturing away from their mother. At such times, they are attractive to silverbacks and to older peers who want to play with them. In my opinion, rough and tumble play is one of the mechanisms for learning how to copulate, and this form of stimulation occurs early in a gorilla's life. We don't know if direct genital contact from mother gorillas is common in nature, but in the zoo, all great ape taxa have been observed mounting and thrusting against the genitalia of their newborns. When I first observed it, I was tempted to call it abnormal, but Professor Davenport called me on it by asking: "How do you know it's abnormal?" Of course, we didn't have norms for such things in the early days of zoo research, and this behavior was not documented by previous investigators in research settings. We should never underestimate the power of the affectional system of mother apes and their infants. I came to understand that there is a functional utility in this obscure and previously undocumented behavior pattern.

PIONEERS OF PRIMATOLOGY

Students of primatology are always surprised when they learn that the first observations of wild apes were conducted by psychologists (Maple, 1979b). Yerkes protegees H. E. Bingham, Henry Nissen, and C. Ray Carpenter studied gorillas, chimpanzees, and orangutans long before zoologists made the journey. Their research was short term, conducted with subjects before they were properly habituated to human observers. In Bingham's case, he found nests and counted feces, but he saw very few gorillas, and all were at a distance. Much later, George Schaller (1963) provided the first detailed account of mountain gorilla behavior in the wild, and his success paved the way for Dian Fossey's longer-term study at the Karisoke field site in Rwanda (Fossey, 1972; 1983).

From these sources, we know that gorillas grow up in a socially stimulating and environmentally rich habitat surrounded by their own kind. They actively forage for the abundant food sources and construct nests where they rest together at night. Other than the occasional leopard, gorillas only fear humankind, the one species that relentlessly pursues them. They live a peaceful, complex social life punctuated by moments of crisis when they are stalked by human hunters. From Willie B.'s size when he was captured, we can only guess how much socialization he received—likely twelve to twenty-four months of care from his mother. This is actually the most critical developmental period for nonhuman primates, so he may have been inoculated by early maternal attachment that prepared him for a social life. We still have many questions about his early experience that remain unanswered. We would need to introduce him to other zoo gorillas to see if Willie B. would recover his social skills. Although he lacked a normal history of species-appropriate socialization, it appears that he played with zookeepers frequently until he was too strong to interact safely with them. We don't know much about his early days at the zoo, but I give credit to those who managed his transition when he was just a baby. If anyone who worked with him during those early days can produce a diary, I would love to read it.

I wasn't the first zoo director who envisioned a partnership with Emory University's Yerkes National Primate Research Center. The first professional zoo director hired by the city was John Roth, a Swiss protege of Hediger, who met with Dr. Bourne in 1968 to seriously discuss opportunities to breed Willie. Unfortunately, the city could not come up with the necessary funds to expand his living quarters, nor could they fulfill many of the promises they made to Mr. Roth when he was hired. He left the zoo after only two years of service.

With the passage of time, Willie's full social potential would eventually emerge. From his playful interactions with zoo visitors, his focus on people may have been a good omen or a bad one. Only time and opportunity would tell, but we were committed from the beginning to a plan that would give him the best chance to succeed socially. The only thing we needed to test our ideas was the availability of other gorillas and sufficient space to encourage interaction. We knew that this would be an opportunity that may only come once in his lifetime, so we did our best to explore all of our options. Fortunately, our world-class landscape architects envisioned an outdoor habitat with all the flexibility and opportunity we needed for Willie to thrive. With their experience as innovators, Jon Coe and Gary Lee were prepared to advance the standards for gorillas well beyond previous norms. As I promised my friends in Dearborn, the Ford African Rain Forest exhibit was and still is second to none.

Our plan for socialization was based on a history of research with laboratory primates. Harlow had conducted exhaustive experiments with rhesus monkeys to demonstrate the importance of social bonds (Harlow, 1971). He called these bonds affectional systems. Among these he identified the mother/infant, infant/mother, heterosexual, and paternal affectional systems. He manipulated softness, movement, and temperature to determine what the critical variables were in facilitating attachments. From these experiments, he determined that "contact comfort" was the factor that calmed young monkeys even when the surrogate model was inanimate. Harlow discovered that "motherless" mothers were socially inadequate and prone to develop abnormal behavior patterns he labeled "deprivation acts." Deprivation acts included self-biting and other forms of auto-aggression, catatonic rocking, even head-banging. Such monkeys also exhibited social deficits; they failed to breed, and if they were subjected to a forced copulation, they neglected their offspring. In one case study, I described the abnormal behavior of a male monkey that was able to briefly copulate, but at a certain intensity interrupted the event with self-biting (Maple, 1974).

Discussions with my colleagues at Yerkes began in earnest soon after I returned from my nine-month sabbatical in New Orleans. I entered into collaboration with Dr. Kenneth Gould, a Yerkes scientist and member of the board of the Atlanta Zoological Society. Ken foresaw great opportunity in our plan for an innovative gorilla exhibit at the zoo. Keys to our planning included a gift of per diem support from zoo benefactor Jay Crouse, who donated sufficient funding to secure the gorilla loan for the two years it would take to design and build the exhibit in Atlanta. There were other accredited institutions from Columbus to Tampa that were strongly interested in acquiring more gorillas, so we had to protect our investment. I likened it to real estate earnest money. To get the attention of our colleagues at Yerkes, we had to demonstrate that we were seriously committed. Had we not raised the millions of dollars required to design and build our flagship exhibit, Mr. Crouse's money would have been wasted.

There was a time, before I was appointed zoo director, when I thought some other institution was going to be first to build the best gorilla habitat, but as fate would have it, I was the right person to shape the vision for the

Ford African Rain Forest. To do it right, I had to satisfy taskmasters like Fred King, who demanded that Yerkes receive equal recognition in the media, and Ford executives, who demanded the blue Ford logo be just the proper shade, no lighter, no darker. Although we always mentioned our Yerkes partners when reporters interviewed my staff, they often failed to include this information when the stories were published or presented on the radio or on television. Ford executives were strict guardians of the Ford image, and I learned a lot about marketing from them. Somehow, I managed to balance these demands and everyone was happy in the end. Our televised debut on WSB-Channel 2 was a huge success, with a massive audience watching Willie B. as he explored his new habitat for the first time. The pride of our collective authorship was on display as we introduced our new facility to the city.

Chapter 4

THE FORD AFRICAN RAIN FOREST

FIGURE 4-1. FORD AFRICAN RAIN FOREST IN FULL BLOOM (M. P. HOFF).

In the four decades that my students and I have studied gorillas, one of the most challenging design problems was the issue of comfort. What defines comfort in zoo gorillas, and how do you factor it into your plan? When Mike Hoff and I wrote *Gorilla Behavior*, I asked a number of field scientists what word they would use to describe the sensation of living in a rain forest substrate. The most common response was "flexible." The thick forest vegetation flexes when gorillas turn the living plants into sleeping nests, and they use the saplings and bushes to locomote on the ground and in the arboreal network of pathways. When youngsters fall in the rain forest during exuberant play bouts, they land on a soft surface that breaks their fall. Exhibit designers try to replicate this environment in the zoo, but it is difficult to achieve. Many city zoos provided only hard infrastructure with cement and tile floors. When females with offspring used climbing structures in these hard environments, they put their fragile offspring at risk. A number of baby gorillas at New York's Bronx Zoo were accidentally dropped or fell, which severely injured or killed them. Bronx curators were so concerned that they made the policy decision to routinely pull babies from their mothers in the first few days of their lives to be raised by human caregivers in a safer environment. In this case, the limitations of living in a cage influenced the social development of young gorillas, threatening them with social deprivation.

This became a big issue when the Association for Zoos and Aquariums set up their Species Survival Plans (SSPs) for a variety of animals. One of the first committees formed was the gorilla SSP. Most of the elected members were prominent directors and veterinarians, but there were two behavioral scientists, myself and Ben Beck. It took a few years for us to successfully persuade this group of silverback stakeholders that the best practice was to ensure that gorillas are raised by their mothers in a species-appropriate social group (Maple and Hoff, 1982; Beck and Power, 1988). This recommendation was based on the model of gorilla social life described in the publications of field scientists.

Although a social group is the most important feature of gorilla life, I've long believed that the hard substrate of many traditional zoos was another risk factor that was inferior to naturalistic, soft substrates (Maple, 1979a). Whenever gorillas need to rest, they look uncomfortable on cement floors. To compensate, zoos usually provide nesting material such as hay, straw, or excelsior for comfort. It is even better if we can provide dirt, edible plants, and grass on at least some of the habitat they occupy. To keep them happy and busy, the zoo's horticulture staff must be prepared to constantly replenish the manmade ecosystem by cutting and collecting browse and distributing it throughout the zoo. For much of his life, Willie B. could not go outdoors, although indoor/outdoor exhibits are preferred. Even cold-weather zoos in cities like Chicago have elected to build outdoor options for apes when the weather permits. The approach of Dr. Beck and I was strongly supported by Gorilla SSP Chairman Dr. Lester E. Fischer. During his tenure as CEO of Lincoln Park Zoo, the ape facilities were vastly improved. Since he retired, his successors have devoted research space within the Regenstein Center for African Apes to operate the Lester E. Fisher Center for the Study and Conservation of Great Apes. With these unique facilities in place, Lincoln Park Zoo has become one of the most important great ape research facilities in the world. As this book goes to press, I am happy to report that Dr. Fischer has just celebrated his one hundredth birthday. No one has been a better friend of gorillas.

THE VERTICAL DIMENSION

Gorillas are large creatures, capable of climbing but not exclusively arboreal. The orangutan, by contrast, is an animal that prefers to occupy the forest canopy. They are the largest primates that live in trees. In captive enclosures with hard floors, orangs take more risks with their offspring. In their former hard habitats at the Atlanta Zoo, experienced mothers routinely climbed to the top of a twenty-foot steel climbing structure and encouraged babies to hold on to the bars. When the offspring were a little older, mothers would locomote independently with their offspring dangling behind them. It was as if they were teaching them to adapt to an arboreal life. Unlike my experience with gorillas, I never witnessed an orangutan baby that fell to the floor.

After our outdoor exhibit was opened, orangutans could climb to a height of fifty-four feet on a modified dead tree surrounded by grass and plants. In other zoos that encourage arboreality, orangs clearly enjoy locomotion above the crowds that observe them from below, and they rarely descend to the ground. National Zoo designers pioneered arboreality for apes in their "O-Line" vertical habitat. Since this exhibit opened, many other zoos have engineered arboreal pathways so apes can actually explore the zoo from the treetops. Philadelphia Zoo installed elevated horizontal travel tubes so the apes (and other animals) can safely travel significant distances from their home enclosures. These innovations also encourage zoos to permit some animals to remain outdoors at night when many zoos are open for special events. The Singapore Zoo pioneered night safaris by specializing in animals that are active at night; elephants, rhinos, tigers, and fishing cats, for example. When designed and operated properly, night exhibits are a form of environmental enrichment for zoo animals.

DEFEATING HARD ARCHITECTURE

In his cement and tile cage, constrained by steel bars for twenty-nine years, comfort was not a factor in Willie B.'S daily life. He had his favorite positions on the elevated platforms, but this urban space was the epitome of hard architecture. I believe his cage was a major contributor to the public's perception that he was incarcerated against his will. Visitors universally felt sorry for him, but this changed quickly when the zoo articulated a new vision and built the Ford African Rain Forest Exhibit, thereby liberating Willie and the thirteen Yerkes gorillas. How this unique exhibit evolved is an interesting story. Many experts and many community leaders committed the zoo to significant reform, the most important being a change from hard to soft architecture.

Regrettably, our innovations in designing outdoor forest simulations did little to improve the hard infrastructure of their night quarters. For safety and security reasons, gorillas must return to indoor confinement to receive their evening meal and spend the night. The great European zoologist, Jeremy Mallinson, once observed that gorillas spend two-thirds of their lives in their night house. He considered it shameful that we hadn't figured out how to bring the same quality inside that we spent millions to create outside. Although Mallinson softened the night houses at Jersey Wildlife Trust, this is a problem we have left for the next generation of zoo designers to ponder and resolve. We've improved night houses by providing more space, but we can do better. When the night house door is opened and they eagerly enter, we will know that we've hit the mark.

In the 1960s, during Willie's infancy, zoos throughout the world competed to acquire charismatic megafauna such as gorillas. Because it was difficult to keep them alive and a challenge to acquire them in Africa, many zoos had to settle for a single gorilla living in a small cage. Isolation reinforced the image of fierce, hostile silverbacks.

FIGURE 4-2. NIGHT HOUSES SOFTENED WITH WOODWOOL. (DEWAR WILDLIFE TRUST)

Gorillas were consistently portrayed in literature and film as fearsome creatures, a smaller version of King Kong. The best example of this image was Gargantua, a huge male exhibited at the Ringling Brothers winter quarters in Sarasota, Florida. He had been mistreated during his capture and suffered an injury to his face that turned into a formidable scar. It all added up to one hostile ape, and the circus did all they could to market his nasty personality. If you went to the circus, you had to pay homage to the awesome Gargantua. Unfortunately, Gargantua helped to brand the image of gorillas as dangerous, hostile creatures. The circus hyperbole was consistent with the experience of the early European explorers in Africa, who universally agreed that gorillas were among the most dangerous African animals.

As we later learned from long-term scientific field studies, gorillas are in fact peaceful animals that become aggressive only when threatened. Visitors to the Virunga Volcanoes region in Central Africa can sit quietly in the presence of silverbacks and their family groups of gorillas without fear of an attack. These tourist groups and a number of dedicated research groups have been successfully habituated to human beings. Tourists pay large sums for the privilege of sitting quietly among a family group. However, should they be seriously threatened, by the approach of poachers, for example, adult males become formidable fighters. Gorillas know the difference between friendly tourists and hostile poachers, and they respond accordingly. From field experience, we learned that zoo gorillas can be safely confined and managed in groups.

LANDSCAPE IMMERSION

In my role as a professor teaching environmental psychology, I have become an evaluator of naturalistic zoo exhibits first introduced in North America by the Jones & Jones architecture firm in Seattle. Their firm introduced the term "landscape immersion." This construct specified that the animal, the landscape, and the visitor must become one. Because we were committed to building the world's best gorilla exhibit in Atlanta, we hired Jon Coe and Gary Lee to plan an exhibit that would be superior to all others. I learned about the expertise of these two landscape architects when I visited Seattle to see the innovative Woodland Park Zoo gorilla exhibit. Jon Coe was working for Jones & Jones at the time of my visit. Coe & Lee was a newly formed design firm by the time we were ready to design and build in Atlanta. Both principals and their partners at Coe & Lee were brilliant. Better yet, they listened to the zoo director, his staff, and the experts we brought to the table to offer their ideas. We all bought into the conclusion that the natural world was the only appropriate model for zoo architecture, and we aimed to simulate if not replicate nature at the new zoo. The high visibility of Zoo Atlanta contributed to the growing reputation of Coe & Lee. And their good reputation elevated ours. It was the perfect symbiotic relationship.

Early in my academic career, long before I was appointed to direct the zoo, I used images of Willie B. and other confined apes to illustrate the way that hard architecture distorts behavior. The published works of Robert Sommer, professor of psychology at UC Davis, were the drivers of these applications. Professor Sommer was my most important graduate school mentor. His suggestion in 1970 that I carefully read the books and papers of Heini Hediger was the best advice I ever received in graduate school. Many years later, I videotaped an interview with Hediger to share his ideas with my peers. Sommer passed the torch to me, and now I gladly pass it on to a newer generation of young scientists and zoo professionals. The thirty-five-minute interview is available on YouTube. His classic book *Man and Animal in the Zoo* inspired the interview and provided a framework for the journal *Zoo Biology*. With Hediger and Sommer on my mind, I embarked on a crusade to improve primate housing and husbandry in research centers and zoos.

Sommer and Hediger discovered many useful principles that increased our understanding of how animals and human beings used space. In a benchmark publication in *Natural History Magazine*, Sommer (1972) offered a stinging critique of the hard architecture that defined traditional zoos. He expanded on this theme in an important book *Tight Spaces* (Sommer, 1972). During graduate school and early in my academic career, I was fortunate that Bob took an interest in my research as he mentored me on the history and the literature of environmental psychology.

Once I moved to Georgia Tech, after three years at Emory University, I began a long-term collaboration with College of Architecture Professors Jean Wineman and Craig Zimring. They too were influenced by Sommer's ideas, and the three of us found opportunity in the *tabula rasa* that the zoo represented. We used the changes that were occurring there to teach our students, and we addressed the need to learn as much as we could from the reforms that were taking place. Professor Wineman published some important papers based on the work of her students at the College of Architecture (Wineman and Choi, 1991; Wineman et al., 1996).

Zoo Atlanta's first major exhibit was unique for its size and complexity. We devoted four acres to five contiguous habitats, each comprised of a silverback and his family group of adult females. Initially, Willie B. had a small habitat to himself in the midst of the others. He was in the perfect position to attract neighboring females, and he was successful in doing so. His keepers met the demand by introducing him carefully to one then another female over time until he had established dominion over his own harem. Thus, Zoo Atlanta was the first zoo in the world to exhibit contiguous breeding groups that represented a "population" of gorillas. It also became a living laboratory or field station for students and faculty to learn about the primacy of environment and behavior.

Professors Wineman and Zimring were innovators who greatly influenced my thinking and helped to guide my students with special interests in the research methodology of post-occupancy evaluation, or POE. Architects and builders advocate POE so they can understand if the building works the way they intended. Zoo directors often claim an exhibit is perceived a certain way or that the animal's life is improved, but they rarely back up these statements with evidence. To justify the million-dollar exhibits in modern zoos today, we think a POE is necessary. Likewise, donors and sponsors want to know that their investment made a difference.

Jackie Ogden's study of Willie B.'s transition from hard to soft habitat was one of the first of many POE studies the students in my lab completed in a number of zoological settings, including Audubon Zoo, San Diego Zoo, and Zoo Atlanta. One of the surprising findings of the Ogden study was the discovery that the gorillas from Yerkes actually preferred to sit on hard surfaces rather than grass. With time, they became more comfortable with natural materials underfoot, but old habits are apparently hard to break.

Sadly, we lost Bob Sommer recently before many of my students had the opportunity to meet him. He was 91. Thankfully, a few of them participated in an EDRA session in Orlando where Bob spoke, and they will always remember the quality time he spent with them. Thanks to Bob Sommer's network of collaborators, I became friends with Heini Hediger. Just before Hediger passed away, I had the privilege of meeting him for breakfast in Switzerland. I told him I wanted to bring some students to meet with him. He didn't think he had much to say to the new generation of students and young zoo biologists, but I strongly disagreed with him. He and Sommer will keep on teaching as long as we take the time to read their books and papers. I have the best memories of sharing with Bob how he and Hediger influenced my thinking. They were major change agents who mediated the evolution and advanced the cause of zoo animal welfare.

Given the prominence of social distancing during the Covid pandemic, I believe the ideas of Hediger and Sommer will prove useful for planning space in future zoos. Distancing, a staple of the Covid era, may have consequences if the six-foot social distance metric continues to be enforced. Greater distance defeats the intimacy of a zoo experience just as it makes waiting rooms in airports more stressful. Close configurations of seating may help travelers to communicate with others who may share their fear of flying. It is clear to me that Sommer's research on personal space will become important in a new way as we craft zoos with different standards and practices suitable to the challenge of resisting viral agents. The metrics of personal space, honed by ethologists, must now be reconsidered and reexamined by social scientists working in public spaces. Landscape immersion may be less effective when people are widely dispersed.

FIGURE 4-3. SOFT ARCHITECTURE IN A LIVING RWANDAN FOREST (J. D. FOWLER).

AUDUBON ZOO—OUR FIRST POE

At the Audubon Zoo, we collaborated with anthropology professor Elizabeth Smithgall Watts and her students at Tulane University. The animals taught an unforgettable lesson to the architects of these naturalistic exhibits when they tore up the new sod and exotic plantings, which were not given sufficient time to root. It was an expensive mistake for the zoo, but the orangutans and the gorillas clearly enjoyed the enriching materials unwittingly provided for them. Jon Coe and Gary Lee taught me to give vegetation a six-month lead before animals can be introduced. Zoos investing in new facilities must be ready to protect and replant materials if they are devoured by the apes. A daily supply of movable browse is one way to protect the planted material. Protecting horticulture requires a vigilant staff. At Zoo Atlanta, our horticulture specialist, Don Jackson, was

44

particularly effective. He was also well-read and regularly published in the botanical and horticulture literature (Jackson, 1990).

The behavior of the Audubon Zoo orangutans and gorillas corroborated an earlier study by Susan Fisher Wilson (1982), who discovered that apes in European zoos were activated by the presence of immovable objects. The opportunity to manipulate the vegetation in the newly landscaped exhibit generated a lot of activity. It is tragic that Willie B., comfortably living among his own kind in a thick rain forest environment, was violently captured and translocated to a barren cage as an infant. He spent the next twenty-nine years on concrete and tile until the Atlanta community found the resources and the will to create a simulated rain forest to rehabilitate and socialize him. Thankfully, he was able to enjoy a natural, social life for the thirteen years he spent in the company of gorillas and people.

While Professor Watts' Tulane students worked with me to evaluate the Audubon exhibit for gorillas and orangutans, I learned about the strengths and weaknesses of this exhibit. The design team was led by the local firm of Cashio and Cochran. Key contributions from Curator David Anderson and a talented keeper staff ensured the exhibit was a successful simulation of a natural habitat. The Audubon exhibits were a huge improvement over hard cages and were aesthetically pleasing, but they were tightly configured. As anyone who has ever lived in New Orleans understands, space is hard to come by, and the zoo was no exception. The space was sufficient for two or three animals, while the audience was a little too close for comfort.

By contrast, in Atlanta as CEO, I was encouraged to develop a vision for one of the largest and certainly one of the world's most complex exhibits for great apes. With the support of the Ford Motor Company, our aspirations drove superior design. My colleagues at Ford insisted that I execute the vision at the high level I had promised when we formed our working partnership. Thankfully, our board of directors agreed with this bold approach. We were, after all, committed to building the world's next great zoo, and the Ford African Rain Forest was the first step in this direction. We modeled the natural world because there were few examples of zoo exhibits that provided the level of innovation and creativity that we required. Hediger was likely the first authority to recommend that nature be the model for all zoo exhibits. In my opinion, his most important design idea was the notion that nature is not a cube; rather, it is curvilinear in form and function. His famed Africa House at Zoo Zurich followed this principle, and we later specified that our Conservation Action Resource Center, designed for people, reflect curvilinear features inside and out.

Archival research and interviews with experts (keepers, curators, scientists, educators) are required to provide the baseline information that drives exhibit planning. As planners, we carefully program exhibits before we design them. There is no substitute for reading the literature about the species and its ecology. The experience of other designers is also consulted, but we avoid the temptation of simply copying other exhibits that have worked well elsewhere.

It is interesting that most of what we know about gorilla behavior was discovered from studies of captive lowland gorillas (*G. g. gorilla*) in zoos and primate research centers. What we know about wild gorillas is largely based on field studies of the mountain gorilla *(G. g. beringei)*. A major difference in the two taxa is their diet (Tutin and Fernandez, 1985).

It is unlikely that we will ever see mountain gorillas or the subspecies *graueri* in zoos. I photographed the zoo world's only documented *graueri* gorillas in Belgium at Antwerp Zoo in 1979. Two *graueri* males, Mbongo and Ngagi, arrived at the San Diego Zoo in 1931. They were studied by the primatologist C. R. Carpenter (1937). A more recent study by McFarland (2007) provided data on a small population of the Cross River gorillas (*G. g. diehli*), the most endangered of the gorilla subspecies. This subspecies is found in a narrow forest on the border of Cameroon and Nigeria. It is estimated that only 300 individuals remain. Thankfully, the Wildlife Conservation Society has enjoyed some success in protecting these animals, and there is evidence that the population is growing.

Unfortunately, there has been little integration of captive experience and field data for gorillas. However, A. H. Harcourt tried to rectify this with a publication in the *International Zoo Yearbook* (Harcourt, 1987). His comments on naturalistic exhibits are especially relevant to zoo design:

> The forest environment of wild gorillas is a complex three-dimensional one, in which the animals spend 45% of their day feeding on over 50 plant species and some invertebrates in a home range of 5 square km or more (Schaller, 1963; Fossey and Harcourt, 1977) . . . In addition, although gorillas are classified as terrestrial, immature animals spend an appreciable amount of time feeding and playing in trees. In the Virungas, 18% of all feeding records of immature animals and 25% of feeding records on the most commonly eaten plant species, *Galium*, were of immatures in trees . . . Feeding in trees might be a way for immatures to avoid competition from the larger and more terrestrial adults (Fossey and Harcourt, 1977).

With information such as this, astute zoo designers build stratified simulations of wild forests that enables the group to share resources and distance themselves when needed. The architects at Jones & Jones reached out to consult with Dian Fossey to review and evaluate their innovative plan for their lowland gorilla exhibit. Photographs taken at the perimeter of the exhibit cannot be distinguished from a wild setting in Rwanda. Success in Seattle inspired the next generation of exhibits, including the Ford African Rain Forest, to simulate nature in every way we could. Not long after our plan was underway, we secured significant funding from the Ford Motor Company. The gift came with a caveat. We had to make good on our pledge to build an exhibit second to none. As Ford marketing executive Jim Donaldson whispered to me when he handed me the first $50,000 check: "It better not be number two!"

The first day that Willie B. set foot in his new habitat was the most important day in the zoo's long history. The media coverage was exhaustive, and he made the pages of *National Geographic Magazine*, the *Washington Post*, and the *New York Times*. Willie's fascination with grass and leaves left the audience in tears. The Yerkes females began to express interest in Willie B. from the earliest moments of their release into the new habitat, just as we had predicted. By patrolling the perimeters, they cautiously approached him, suggesting we may not have to wait long to test his social skills. Perhaps they had greater insight into his potential than we did.

Chapter 5

SIMULATING THE NATURAL WORLD

Zoo Atlanta's Ford African Rain Forest exhibit was immediately acknowledged for its superior standards and thrust the zoo into a leadership position for innovative design. Other zoo directors traveled to Atlanta to study its unique features, and Coe & Lee were now the hottest zoo design firm in North America. With so many gorillas, Zoo Atlanta was now one of the most influential collections in the world. We were also blessed with talented faculty and students from nearby universities and veterinary schools committed to scientific and medical partnerships far beyond the norms for our profession. Atlanta was the nation's hot spot for the media on gorillas, and scientific publications began to flow at a fast pace. Almost overnight, Zoo Atlanta had become the center of the universe for gorilla biology and behavior. Our breadth and our depth enabled us to examine unique problems and issues, contributing new knowledge for our colleagues. Now that we were design innovators, with a breeding population of gorillas, we began to accumulate knowledge about management and husbandry. Willie B. became a priority for our curators and veterinarians.

Although Willie was not the largest of the adult males we exhibited (Calabar weighed in at 500 pounds), he was 459 pounds when he stepped outside for the first time. With exercise and an improved diet, he began to lose weight under Dr. McManamon's persistent supervision. He was never svelte, but he was fitter than he had been at any point in his adult life at the zoo. Nutrition had become an important subject in zoo medicine, and we entered the field when we hired a master's level nutritionist to monitor and organize new approaches in this domain. Almost immediately, Willie's diet began to change. In the old days when he lived in a cage, Willie ate twice each day. Because zoo animals often resisted confinement in their night quarters, the evening meal was a strong incentive to return when staff called them. In quantity and quality, it was the most nutritious meal of the day. With so much natural space in the Ford African Rain Forest, Willie and the other gorillas spent a lot of their time foraging for small food items distributed by our staff throughout the day. Proper feeding became an important management strategy in the new era of reform.

Our greatest strength was our expertise in reproductive biology. Our partners at Yerkes were focused on reproductive studies of all of our apes, including Willie B. We had more confidence in the reproductive potential of the Yerkes gorillas whose history was known, but we continued to wonder whether Willie B. had the right stuff to become a social, sexual, and eventually a parental gorilla. Our plan always assumed that a superior exhibit would bring out the best in all of the animals. Coe & Lee's commitment to realism matched the evidence-based management philosophy of our highly professional staff and the many brilliant faculty and students who worked among us. The design team was in complete agreement that we would try to design and build the world's best exhibits for gorillas and orangutans. I regret that I couldn't add chimpanzees to the mix because we didn't have the funds or the space to exhibit three great ape species in facilities of equal quality.

As we planned the exhibits, we examined all of the variables that contributed to psychological well-being and good health. One important but often neglected factor was verticality. By expanding spatial volume, primates and other species are provided with new dimensions of complexity and opportunity. Vertical exhibits encourage locomotion, and this ensures a greater degree of fitness. This idea originated as an experiment to improve locomotion in gorillas at *Apenheul* in the Netherlands. I first visited this unique facility in 1980. A decade later, Jon Coe sketched vertical travel tubes that were installed at the Center for Great Apes sanctuary in Wauchula, Florida. This type of cost-effective, elevated trail system has influenced other institutions committed to fitness. Jacksonville Zoo and Gardens opened a tiger exhibit in 2014 with elevated travel tubes. Many species can be trained to utilize these enrichment opportunities. Built to conform to a wellness strategy (Maple and Bocian, 2013), this exhibit won an AZA award for design excellence.

In 2019, I published a paper with Heather Browning on the role of spatial volume in zoo design. To help designers to accurately compare the quantity and quality of exhibits, we offered a mathematical approach to calculating useable space (Browning and Maple, 2019). Useable space is volumetric space, and its complexity can be estimated. Our method was simplified, but computer driven measurement techniques will enable planners to understand the true complexity of habitats that encourage vertical movement.

In Chapter 6 we discuss the strength of gorillas in greater detail. However, when designing exhibits for verticality, we must find materials that are strong enough to withstand the animal's use of the artificial branches we create from steel rebar covered with gunite or shotcrete. Trees created by contractors look incredibly real, but they lack flexibility. On a consulting visit to the Topeka Zoo, I attended the grand opening of the new orangutan exhibit. A large male entered the facility (drum rolls, please) and immediately climbed into the artificial tree. The company that made the tree had guaranteed it would be strong enough to resist the ape's grasp, but they were proved wrong. Much to the chagrin of the zoo director, Gary Clarke, the animal snapped a large branch as if it was a twig. As he continued to dismantle the exhibit, Mr. Clarke made a frantic phone call to the manufacturer. We can conclude that arboreality for the largest and strongest apes requires stringent testing protocols. Of course, the ultimate test occurs the day the animal moves in.

THE ZOO AS EDEN

We pioneered a unique approach to exhibit design in Atlanta when we made our first study visit to the natural habitats we were attempting to simulate at the zoo. Because of the interest expressed by local television station WSB Channel 2, we brought our community along with us as we trekked through East and Central Africa. Jon Coe, the first architect to suggest that naturalistic zoos were a kind of Eden for animals, was one of the stars of this program, and he joined several of our key staff who were involved in the programming and implementation of the plan. The assembled zoo team made a number of programs, traveling through the wild ecosystems of Africa, Australia, and Asia. The program won several local Emmy Awards and led its time slot every time it was offered.

We aimed to teach Atlanta citizens how to think creatively about zoo design so they would understand its connection to the natural world. Jon Coe dug deep into his bag of tricks to show us how he formed a vision for landscapes inspired by nature. I remember him calling attention to trees growing out of the side of riverine habitats. Sure enough, when our exhibit was completed, Jon had executed horizontal trees.

During our visits, we collected an archive of videography to study after our return. This material was very helpful in planning our educational messaging. One of the shows, "Search for the Red Ape," was distributed by the Discovery Channel and enjoyed a long run. On that trip, we were joined by actress and conservationist Stefanie Powers. I received many e-mail messages and phone calls from friends who saw the short clips of this program on airplanes and other venues.

This unique partnership between the zoo and its sponsors was a blend of education, marketing, and science and forms a historical record of our travels. With today's audio-visual technology, anyone can produce quality images with the small cameras and telephones that have replaced the bulky cameras we used in the seventies and eighties. In the future, videography and animation could be used to provide realistic background at interpretive centers as visitors walk into a simulated forest.

Powerful advertising stimuli are currently operating in Japan and China with holographic images. Theme parks and aquariums have also deployed this technology. Motion is enriching for animals and people alike and provides greater realism to enhance the experience of landscape immersion. I'm certain that our technology collaborators at Georgia Tech could help us engineer holographic images of Willie B. himself and return him to his Zoo Atlanta habitat. We have already partnered with them on a virtual reality interpretation of the Ford African Rain Forest exhibit. I would love to introduce a holographic image of Willie B. to his son, the females he lived with, and the other offspring he sired.

NATURALISTIC BARRIERS

Primate center veterinarians and scientists have experimented with translocating surplus apes to zoos and semi-natural habitats for many years (Wilson and Elicker, 1976). In 1975, several gorillas, orangutans, and chimpanzees were loaned by Yerkes to the local Lion Country Safari Park in Stockbridge, Georgia, for exhibition on small island habitats. Unfortunately, several of the animals drowned, and the others were eventually removed. When my students and I began to work with a small group of chimpanzees that remained, we designed and built a chain link barrier fence just below the water line that surrounded the island as a last-resort security measure for any animals that ventured too far into the water (Clarke, Juno and Maple, 1982). For the duration of their exhibition, no animals were lost to drowning. Cages were so inadequate that we were all experimenting with new ways of containment in those days. Outdoor exhibits were perceived as vastly superior by our guests, who appreciated our commitment to realism.

Worldwide, many naturalistic exhibits deploy water moats as a means of separating the animals from the visitors. When I was working in New Orleans, I decided to take a look at the history of gorillas in water. I worked with a Tulane graduate student named Susan Brown and her mentor, Professor Bill Dunlap. In my survey of the literature, I learned that lowland gorillas will enter water when feeding in shallow swampland. In the zoo, some gorillas choose to enter the water by immersing themselves in streams or waterfalls. Shallow water is relatively safe, as Figure 5-1 illustrates (Brown, Dunlap and Maple, 1982). Susan's study demonstrated that the most important variable controlling this behavior in New Orleans was humidity. Water features can be good for apes, but only with experience can they know how dangerous water can be.

A report by Golding (1972) documented young gorillas at the Ibadan Zoo in Africa and their propensity to play in shallow, water-filled moats at the perimeter of the enclosure. The exhibit was carefully engineered to protect the gorillas, and they learned to float and propel themselves through water while playing. Recent field studies of mountain gorillas in Uganda provided evidence of solitary water play in a subadult and two adults (Costa et al., 2018). The investigators suggested that exploration of water sources benefited gorillas by preparing them to utilize water sources for drinking and playing and for developing resilience for challenges that the complex natural environment may present. Moving water is also a calming stimulus for visitors, and likely for gorillas as well.

Had Willie lived in a soft, naturalistic, social environment for the first twenty-nine years of his life, avoiding the stress of isolation and confinement, who knows how long he would have lived, and how many offspring he would have sired? There is some solace in the fact that we eventually rescued Willie B. from an impoverished life, and my zoo colleagues have rescued nearly all suffering gorillas, at least in those institutions that enjoy the standards and best practices of an AZA accreditation. The saga of Willie B. symbolizes the successful reforms of a zoo revolution in Atlanta and throughout North America, if not the world. The reforms that have liberated zoo gorillas must now be extended to include other animals living in restricted conditions. We know how to rehabilitate and resocialize non-human primates, and these techniques should be tested on other species. Some animals are resistant to isolation. Lions, for example, hand-raised by human caregivers, usually respond to social opportunity by mating in adulthood. However, like monkeys and apes, big cats and bears are not resistant to stereotypies. Back-and-forth pacing in their small enclosures is always perceived as abnormal behavior. Naturalistic habitats and social opportunities usually reduce the frequency of stereotypy, but they do not eliminate it.

THE MENTAL HOSPITAL MODEL

My experience working in California mental hospitals during my under-graduate years at the University of the Pacific was useful for my later work in zoos. Mental hospitals and prisons represented the extremes of hard architecture. In those days, traditional zoos had more in common with mental hospitals than with nature. Many research papers made this com-parison, including the observations of Heini Hediger (Ellenberger, 1960; Hediger, 1950; Sommer, 1974; Sommer, 2008). Many of the abnormal be-havior patterns observed in confined monkeys and apes were also observed in people, including self-injurious behavior.

FIGURE 5-1. USEABLE WATER SOURCE IN NEW ORLEANS. (T. MAPLE).

Although I occasionally worked as a consultant to design firms, I was in greater demand as a "counselor" for failed social relationships—for ex-ample, apes that would not socialize, persistent hyper-aggression, depres-sion, and failure to breed or parent normally. It was no surprise to me that many of these problems were due to animals that were simply incompatible. When you changed partners, the relationships were frequently better. But the main problem before zoo curators fully understood ape biology and behavior were inappropriate social groupings. Certainly, singleton males, a common feature of traditional zoos, would never produce normal behavior, but pairs of apes were no better because apes (with the exception of gibbons and siamangs, so-called lesser apes) don't live that way in nature. When housed with one female, males might aggressively assault their cagemates, leading to injuries and even deaths. A male's mortal wounding of a female cagemate was documented at the Sacramento Zoo in 1980.

The most important shift in North American ape management was the profession's recognition that we had to set up species-appropriate groups to stimulate normal social behavior and social development. To do this, we needed more apes and more space, so breeding became a priority. To activate Willie B.'s social potential, the first step was to acquire additional gorillas. Willie B. needed the Yerkes gorillas, and they needed him to provide the incentive to build a complex, naturalistic habitat where they all could thrive. Except for those living in a compound at the Yerkes Field Station, all of the Yerkes gorillas were living in hard, restricted enclosures not much different from Willie's cage at the zoo. It pleased me that all of the gorillas would eventually be able to go outdoors and locomote on a soft substrate. The planned zoo habitats would therefore be liberating for all of them. I had waited for this outcome since I first wrote a scathing critique of hard zoos and labs for the book *Captivity and Behavior* (1989), edited by primatologist Joe Erwin.

In the first decade of my career, I was exposed to a universe of dysfunctional environments and animals that could not emit natural behaviors. Environmental constraints included a failure to provide usable vegetation, an absence of social companions, and rigid, unimaginative feeding schedules. These environments were so bad that you might conclude they were purposely designed for failure.

Chapter 6

PSYCHOBIOLOGY OF GORILLAS

My graduate education integrated biology and psychology in the specialized field of developmental psychobiology. Also known as biological psychology, it is a subfield of biology and psychology that deals with the interaction between biological and social phenomena. Robert Yerkes described himself as a psychobiologist. In this chapter, I will selectively review the biological foundation of behavior for wild and zoo gorillas.

We can better understand Willie B., or any other individual for that matter, when we learn about its natural history, physical characteristics, and species-specific habits. Our knowledge of gorillas is incomplete, but we know that there is some variability in the taxa we have identified. Currently, there are two recognized species of gorillas; the western lowland gorilla (*G. gorilla*) and the eastern mountain gorilla (*G. beringei*). A lowland subspecies of western gorilla has been recently identified as the Cross River gorilla (*G. g. diehli*). Grauer's gorilla (*G. b. graueri*) is a local subspecies of the eastern gorilla. New research will identify any significant differences in the behavior of these taxa. Currently, we know that they differ in size, pelage, and diet.

At the California Primate Research Center in Davis, I was presented with the opportunity to study broadly the different stages of life in a variety of primates. Over the years, my publications have ranged from studies of infant monkeys, including observations and experiments focused on communication, courtship, parenting, and cognitive deficits in aged apes. Due to the variety of species available to me and my students, we took a comparative approach in most of our research. I am one of only a few psychologists in North America who have studied all four great ape taxa (bonobos, chimpanzees, gorillas, orangutans). According to Hodos and Campbell (1969), the most meaningful comparisons in psychology are those between closely related species.

Occasionally, scientists can compare the behavior of subspecies. With gorillas (*berengei, diehli, gorilla, grauri*), these studies have not yet been conducted, but our access to these populations will soon make it feasible. With populations of bonobos increasing, zoos will soon be able to compare bonobos to their closest primate relative, the common chimpanzee.

When zoologist George Schaller was preparing for his pioneering study of mountain gorillas, he observed captive lowland gorillas in several zoos. He had to filter their behavior through the prism of hard architecture. Modern zoos such as Bronx, Lincoln Park, and Zoo Atlanta now provide naturalistic facilities that are much more like the natural world. The naturalistic exhibits that characterize revitalized zoos are superior settings for observing gorillas in part because they were planned for groups, not pairs or singletons. The Zoo Atlanta facilities were designed to be a world-class research center for the study and conservation of apes and other species. The best of these new zoos established strong partnerships with field programs. Zoo Atlanta's relationship with Dian Fossey Gorilla Fund International is a good example of what can be done with mutual support. The current CEO of DFGFI, Dr. Tara Stoinski, has significantly expanded the scope of activities in Africa, but she has also retained her interest in the science of conservation. Fossey's camp has never been more productive thanks to Tara's careful stewardship.

We had research and management in mind when Mike Hoff and I wrote *Gorilla Behavior*. The audience we envisioned was comprised of graduate students, veterinarians, curators, caregivers, architects, and conservation biologists. Our primary purpose in writing the book was to provide zoos and research centers the knowledge and perspective they needed to deliver a better quality of life for gorillas like Willie B. I am confident that my peers in the zoo world know exactly how to provide superior facilities for all ape taxa. An examination of North America's best outdoor gorilla exhibits makes this point.

FIGURE 6-1. *G. GRAUERI* SUBSPECIES, ANTWERP ZOO IN 1979 (TERRY L. MAPLE).

AGING APES

At forty-one, Willie B. was old enough at his death to be a subject in an aging study. New facilities and advances in health care have enabled all apes to live longer and better lives in the zoo. It is surprising that more studies have not been conducted on the effects of age since apes are so close to humanity in their basic biology. A review by Bloomsmith et al. (2002) found only a few studies of aged great apes. One study by Kate Baker (2003) revealed that aged chimpanzees over the age of 40 were less aggressive, less manipulative, and moved around their enclosure at a slower rate than younger animals. Older females also emitted more submissive behaviors than their younger counterparts.

No other studies of aging apes had been reported until Bloomsmith filed her master's thesis (1982). Bloomsmith studied the behavior of two chimpanzees, ages 50 and 52 years, at the Yerkes National Primate Research Center. At the time of the study, these were the two oldest chimpanzees in North America. One of them, Gamma, lived to the age of 59. The record for males was set by Philadelphia Zoo's Massa, was set recently by the male Ozoum, currently living at Zoo Atlanta at the ripe old age of 60. He is the first lowland gorilla in a North American zoo to reach his sixth decade of life, but he seems healthy enough to live much longer. Of all the silverbacks we acquired from Yerkes, "Ozzie" was the most physically fit. He is a remarkable specimen who seems to have greatly benefitted from his new life outdoors.

FIGURE 6-2. OZOUM, OLDEST LIVING MALE GORILLA. (ZOO ATLANTA).

The Bloomsmith manuscript, reviewing five simple learning and memory tasks, failed to demonstrate a universal, age-related decline in cognitive performance. It should be noted that Bula andGamma had spent their entire lives as subjects in the Yerkes research population. It is known that experienced apes perform better than those without relevant experience. We've now studied chimpanzees and gorillas in their forties and fifties and found little evidence of decline. It may be the case that great apes in their forties and fifties are not yet really old. In the last eight years of his life, Willie B. was not very different than he was in his earlier years. I am hopeful that animals in retirement at zoological sanctuaries will be permitted to enter a subject pool to enable further evaluation of age-related cognitive deficits.

It is fortunate that aging became an important subject in psychology during my time in academia. My students were also able to learn from colleagues at the Georgia Tech College of Architecture who specialized in generating new ideas to help disabled citizens. As far as I know, no one has looked at how traditional zoo architecture impedes the ambulatory behavior of aging apes, but it is a subject that should be examined. The soft architecture recommended by Robert Sommer is surely easier on the joints than cement and steel caging. Since apes appear to retain their social status regardless of their age, they all need to live in comfortable quarters.

My lab became involved in aging studies at the invitation of my colleague Joe Erwin, who has carried out collaborative research with some of the nation's most important neuroscientists. Joe brokered the brains of gorillas when they died in zoos and made sure they reached the specialized labs where they could be studied by experts. Knowledge in this area is rapidly advancing with the close cooperation of zoo veterinarians, neuroscientists, and comparative psychologists. Zoo Atlanta's success with longevity will ensure that affiliated scientists focused on aging will make new discoveries as the Zoo Atlanta gorillas continue to grow older. If a sufficient number of them reach an age that reveals deficits, they will be a very valuable resource.

During the time that Bloomsmith studied aged chimpanzees at Yerkes, we began to worry that the aging gorilla Massa would die before anyone had the opportunity to study him. Thankfully, Philadelphia Zoo executives encouraged our participation in an observational comparison of Massa (at nearly 54) and our gorilla Willie B. (24 years at the time of the study). This is the only source of

information on aging effects with Massa as the subject. In his fifties, Massa did not reveal any obvious cognitive or behavioral defects. To fill the gaps in our knowledge, it will be important for us to carry out formal cognitive studies of all gorillas in this age category.

SIZE AND STRENGTH

Willie B. was a very large gorilla with a massive head. By gorilla standards, he was quite handsome. We know this, in part, because of the positive response of neighboring females who demonstrated their interest by moving closer to him at the edge of the moats dividing his habitat from theirs. Presumably, the silverback's great size and strength evolved to defend the group from predators and poachers, but also to intimidate other males trying to test the alpha leader. Scientists at the Dian Fossey Gorilla Fund carried out a joint research project with colleagues at the Max Planck Institute and George Washington University in a study of mountain gorillas.

FIGURE 6-3. MASSIVE BACK AND NECK OF A LOWLAND SILVERBACK (GETTYS).

Data from this study supported the idea that male size and strength is attractive to females. Examining the efficacy of a composite measure of the crest and back, the investigators found that this statistic correlated with the achievement of dominance, the number of females that joined his group, and how long the animal was able to maintain his position in the group.

While there may be other variables contributing to their success, gorillas with higher crest-back scores were more aggressive, and this led to greater reproductive success. It is unfortunate that as formidable as silverbacks appear, they are no match for heavily armed poachers. They evolved to defend their kind against lesser foes, but the introduction of lethal weapons created a mismatch.

Size is certainly important in the courtship process, and it plays out clearly in the zoo. We began to think of Willie B. as a breeder when we noticed females from neighboring groups spending time close to his enclosure. Their attention suggested they found him attractive, and their behavior emboldened us to form a new group with Willie B. as the silverback leader. We know firsthand that Willie B. was strong. In the late seventies, volunteers and keepers set up a tug-of-war game for Willie. The tug-of-war idea was the brainchild of Jack Throp, formerly director of Honolulu Zoo. He set up a tug-of-war apparatus outside the cage of his silverback so visitors could feel how strong he was. Under supervision, the experience was exhilarating, but keepers had to be careful that the big male didn't pull the smaller human contestant too close to the bars of his cage. Willie B. could hold off a dozen men just by putting his foot on the rope. He was devious too. When the people relaxed their grip, he suddenly pulled the rope away from them, pulling them down in a heap. He seemed to enjoy these encounters with his fans and friends. In the days of solitary gorillas in a permanent state of boredom, we coped by therapeutic interventions such as tug-of-war games.

The one feature all apes have in common is their great strength. If the highly emotional chimpanzee had the devious persistence of the orangutan and the strength of gorillas, it would be a very dangerous animal indeed, and much more capable of escape. Compared to human beings, the superior strength of apes has been consistently confirmed but generally overestimated. They are certainly stronger than we are, but not to the extent once believed.

The first objective study was conducted in 1923 at the Bronx Zoo when John Bauman deployed a dynamometer to measure the strength of apes. Although the chimpanzees in his study were reluctant subjects, one female pulled 1,260 pounds on the device. A large male chimpanzee at the zoo, Boma, pulled 847 pounds with one hand. As a professor at a small college, Bauman had access to human subjects on the football team. The strongest humans in his comparative study pulled a maximum of 500 pounds with both hands. Another study conducted by a Yale scientist in 1943 found that a male chimpanzee could pull about the same weight as an adult human being. Adjusting for body size, he concluded chimps were only slightly stronger than men.

When comparing apes to humans, it is clear that the massive upper body musculature of chimpanzees, gorillas, and orangutans give them an advantage in overall strength (Hawks, 2009). Unlike bipedal humans, quadrupedal apes are not built for speed. Their legs are strong for jumping up into trees, but they don't support sprinting. The lowland gorilla Shobani performed a vertical jump of 31.5 inches at the Nagoya Zoo in Japan. This was surprising since he weighed four hundred pounds at the time of this test. Combined with its long arms, gorillas are capable of dunking a basketball.

Dr. Terry Todd, a strength expert on the faculty of Auburn University, visited me in 1985. He had written a series of articles for *Sports Illustrated* discussing strong men he had interviewed and observed. Dr. Todd was himself a power lifter who was married to the world's strongest woman, Jan Todd. In an article about the wrestler Andre the Giant (who suffered from a disease known as gigantism), Dr. Todd compared him to a gorilla. For example, his hands were comparable, and he weighed over five hundred pounds. At 7 feet, 5 inches, he was much taller than a gorilla. I thought Dr. Todd would be interested in seeing gorillas up close at Yerkes, and he accepted my invitation. When he saw the silverbacks at Yerkes and Willie B. at the zoo, he remarked that their great strength was apparent in the graceful way they jumped up to sleeping platforms and moved around in their enclosures. It was clear to him that only humans affected by gigantism or pumped up on steroids could compare to the natural strength of an adult male gorilla.

When he served as our curator of education, Jeff Swanagan commissioned a suit of clothes that would have fit Willie B. He and his band of educators would take the coat and pants to schools so the children could appreciate the sheer size of a gorilla. According to Jeff's calculations, if Willie B. wore clothing, he would have needed a size 62 coat. A photograph of Jeff demonstrating Willie B.'s sartorial requirements appears in my book *Zoo Man* (Maple, 1993). When he took the custom-made suit to service clubs, he learned that adults were also fascinated with the great size of silverbacks.

In 1988, during his annual physical, our medical staff collected anthropometric measurements of Willie B. He was 28 years old, six feet tall, and he weighed in at 459 pounds. His waist was 55 inches, and his chest girth was measured at 64 inches. The circumference of his neck was 40 inches. His bicep was 17 inches with a 30-inch total arm length. His wrist was 12 inches, and the length of his hand was 9.5 inches. Willie's arm span was 100 inches. He had 28-inch thighs and 18-inch calves. His ring size was 4 inches. All things considered, Willie B. was a big boy, bigger in fact than the great Gargantua. Of course, big does not mean better as too many gorillas suffer from obesity. You cannot blame the animal for what we feed them. The quality and quantity of food zoos have traditionally fed apes has been wildly incorrect. Proper nutrition enables gorillas to thrive in captivity. A poor diet contributes to poor health and premature mortality.

There is still a lot to learn about the basic biology of gorillas. Their close genetic relationship to humankind makes them susceptible to viruses common to both. Like humans, apes are vulnerable to life-threatening zoonotic diseases such as Ebola. There are other distinct differences between apes and people. For example, human eye morphology is considered to be unique among the primates. Human eyes expose a greater amount of visible sclera, and they have a white sclera due to a lack of pigmentation (Mayhew and Gomez, 2015). Investigators found that many gorillas in their subject pool had scleras similar to those of humans, concluding that white scleras evolved to amplify direct gazes involved in social cognition. This finding suggests that managers could predict the social propensities of gorillas by the characteristics of their scleras. This idea should be investigated.

Another distinct characteristic of gorillas is their body odor. To those of us who spend a lot of time with them, the odor is actually quite pleasant.

It is so strong that zoo visitors know when they are getting close to the gorilla exhibit. A study by Hepper and Wells (2010) sought to discover individually identifiable odors in western lowland gorillas. Human subjects made the fewest errors when identifying the odor of a silverback. They made more errors when they were tested with the odor of young gorillas. The investigators hypothesized that body odor may play a role in gorilla social behavior. Regrettably, it may also serve as a cue that enables poachers to locate gorillas in the dense forests where they live. Poachers do not fear gorillas, so their odor is a welcome indicator that they are getting closer to their victims.

Chapter 7

PROTECTING THE NEXT
GENERATION OF APES

Populations of wild western lowland gorillas are affected by the threat of bushmeat hunting and habitat loss. Commercial logging is also a problem since it opens corridors into remote areas for hunters and poachers. Ebola has also taken its toll, reducing the population of gorillas in Gabon by as much as 50 percent (Walsh, 2003). Due to the severity of these threats, the World Conservation Union has designated western gorillas critically endangered. To correct this dire situation, conservation groups have issued a serious of action plans that are designed to support the survival of western gorillas.

Eastern species, *beringei* and *graueri*, suffer from serious habitat loss due to encroaching agriculture and the activities of poachers. Disease is also a threat. Gorillas succumb to many of the same viral agents as human beings. Willie B.'s keepers had to be careful around him when they were nursing a cold because he was vulnerable to respiratory illnesses spread by coughing or sneezing. In Rwanda, people can be denied the opportunity to visit the habituated tourist groups if a tourist is visibly sick. When gorillas show signs of respiratory illness, the veterinarians assigned to the Karisoke project are prepared to intervene with antibiotics. They are also prepared to provide first aid when a gorilla is wounded by a snare or injured from a fight.

It is very risky to anesthetize a gorilla in the wild or in a zoo, and there have been cases when the animals did not recover from the administration of drugs to immobilize them. Zoo veterinarians prefer to examine them once each year under anesthesia. A list of the diseases that are dangerous to gorillas include the common cold, pneumonia, influenza, hepatitis, smallpox, chicken pox, bacterial meningitis, tuberculosis, measles, rubella, mumps, yellow fever, paralytic poliomyelitis, and encephalomyocarditis. Parasitic diseases also afflict wild gorillas.

ONE MEDICINE/ONE HEALTH

In Africa, many gorillas have died from Ebola, while bushmeat poachers who kill gorillas exposed to Ebola have died from eating gorillas infected with the virus. From 2001 to 2005, more than 5,000 western lowland gorillas in Africa died from Ebola. There is growing concern about pathogens that jump from one host species to another. Hantavirus has jumped from rodents to humans; canine distemper has turned up in populations of lions in the Serengeti.

The most dangerous trend was recently confirmed when gorillas at the San Diego Safari Park tested positive for coronavirus. So far, they have demonstrated only mild symptoms, but the park had to be closed to the public until they recovered. To protect their collection, San Diego Zoo recently vaccinated nine great apes with an experimental vaccine created for animals by a veterinary pharmaceutical company. Coronavirus has also infected tigers in several North American zoos, but, so far, the Covid virus hasn't killed any zoo animals. We used to think there was a species barrier that protected us from these diseases, but the findings indicate that our intimate contact with wildlife is changing the paradigm. Today, more than at any time in history, we recognize the significance of "one medicine," that is, the unity of veterinary and human medicine. Today's wildlife veterinarians often arrange collaborative research projects using both wild and zoo populations. The West Nile virus that affected wild birds was first discovered by a zoo pathologist in wild birds that died on the grounds of the Bronx Zoo.

THE HIGH RISK OF HABITUATION

Increased contact between great apes and humans will likely lead to morbidity and mortality in the apes exposed. Woodford et al. (2002) provided a helpful, detailed list of remedies to the risk associated with habituation. If followed correctly, we can protect these valued creatures from overzealous interventions in the wild and in the zoo. Pandemic virus transmission from humans to apes has been documented in tissue samples from chimpanzees that died during respiratory disease outbreaks in the Tai Research Project in Ivory Coast (Kondgen et al., 2008). As the investigators concluded:

> The close approach of humans to apes, which is central to both research and tourism programs, represents a serious threat to wild apes. This represents a dilemma because both activities have clear benefits for ape conservation.

Dr. Tara Stoinski recently observed that the conservation community was not surprised by the Covid-19 pandemic (Stoinski, 2020). Conservation biologists warned us that the systematic destruction of ecosystems puts both wildlife and humanity at risk. This point of view suggests that we have to do more than simply vaccinate against the latest virus. We must be careful to maintain the delicate balance in a natural world that is home to wildlife and people. We can start by protecting ecosystems while investing in higher living standards for people living near and among vulnerable populations of wild animals and pristine forests. Desperate people will be tempted to exploit gorillas and other wildlife. That is another reason to support tourism. In some remote regions, it is the only source of outside income for the local people.

One person's effort to protect gorillas in Bwindi Impenetrable National Park is the Conservation through Public Health Initiative managed by Uganda veterinarian Gladys Kalema-Zikusoka. There are currently 460 mountain gorillas in this region. During the pandemic, Dr. Kalema-Zikusoka instituted social distancing standards that have been strictly enforced to keep gorillas away from human visitors to the park. In addition, all visitors to the area must wear a mask. People must comply with these regulations because gorillas don't know how to social distance. They congregate in tightly configured family groups, so they live at risk of infection by any virus that quickly spreads among them. Kalema-Zikusoka and her colleagues are hoping to avoid the disaster of a Covid outbreak, but they are prepared to isolate and treat any group that may be infected. These extraordinary precautions have been instituted because tourism is the most important economic driver in the park.

Another remarkable conservation success story is the Gorilla Rehabilitation and Conservation Education Center (GRACE), the world's only sanctuary for Grauer's gorillas. Located in the Democratic Republic of Congo near the Tayna Nature Reserve, GRACE nurses orphans back to health, then gives them a chance to be reunited with other gorillas. The fourteen gorillas at GRACE—all orphans—form a tight-knit surrogate family. The ultimate goal of the program is to reintroduce them into the wild. More than a sanctuary, GRACE works with local communities on conservation education, forest protection, and sustainable livelihoods to help secure a future for all gorillas. An equally important goal is to foster peaceful coexistence between humans and gorillas. Many zoos are supporting GRACE, but its most important benefactor is the Walt Disney Company. Disney sends financial and human resources to support construction and management at the camp.

HEART DISEASE IN ZOO GORILLAS

When zoo gorillas began to die young from heart disease, the medical experts consulting with zoo professionals could not diagnose the cause. However, high stress, restrictive cages, and living too frequently as singletons are likely contributing factors. Chimpanzees in government research facilities have exhibited increases in hypertension due to aging and obesity (Ely et al., 2013). Many gorillas and orangs are classified as obese, and an orangutan at Brookfield Zoo developed diabetes. A study of chronic hypertension with subsequent heart failure in a 28-year-old lowland gorilla recently appeared in the literature (Miller et al., 1999). Electrocardiography detected an enlarged heart among other symptoms.

Zoo veterinarians and consulting nutritionists have suggested that diet may be a mediator in heart disease because we are still learning how to feed gorillas to replicate their diet in nature. For example, field studies have discovered evidence that lowland gorillas prefer fruit to a greater extent than their mountain gorilla cousins (Tutin and Fernandez, 1984). Mountain gorillas consume a lot of fiber by contrast. Lowland gorillas in the zoo are fed browse in addition to traditional garden vegetation such as cabbages, carrots, and the like. From studies in the field, we have also learned to provide greater varieties of food. The microhabitat of gorillas in the forest includes great variety, another good reason to protect plants and animals.

Browse is not only a dietary benefit but also a form of psychological enrichment. To keep gorillas healthy, we may also need to intervene as "personal trainers" to encourage strenuous locomotion. Designers must be more creative in delivering structures that encourage them to climb, run, and work. Fortunately, gorillas eagerly respond to training opportunities. This is another good reason for a zoo to employ applied behavior analysis (ABA) (Maple and Segura, 2014). Many zookeepers have received advanced training in ABA offered through organized workshops by experts in the field.

In the days when he lived behind bars, Willie B.'s keepers used to sprint the length of his cage to activate him, and he clearly enjoyed it. He would follow them, beating his chest, and ending with a body blow on the bars of his cage. It was a frightening display of strength. Designing enclosures to encourage play and locomotion is one of the issues that challenges zoo architects. Our goal should be to keep them from becoming couch potatoes. The photo of Willie B. in Figure 8-1 was published in the *Atlanta Journal-Constitution* on his thirty-second birthday in 1990. He weighed 450 pounds. Amen (2017) described the situation at Cleveland Metroparks Zoo where a cardiac ultrasound revealed that the male lowland gorilla Bebac was suffering from heart disease at the age of twenty-four. Soon thereafter, Makolo was also diagnosed with heart disease. He was only twenty-one at the time. Human heart medication, beta blockers, and ACE inhibitors were not effective in treating their symptoms. Both gorillas were obese, and they had developed abnormal behaviors such as regurgitation and reingestion (R&R).

FIGURE 8-1. WILLIE B. IN A COMFORTABLE POSE (WILLIAM BERRY/AJC).

Curators at the zoo observed that Makolo and Bebac received several servings of nutritional cookies with grain, starch, and sugar as the standard ingredients. This diet of processed, calorie-dense food was nowhere near the natural diet of wild gorillas. Such eating habits are known to be detrimental to the health of human beings. The remedy suggested by Conservation and Research Curator Dr. Kristen Lukas eliminated the starchy diet and replaced it with large amounts of vegetables, green beans, dandelion greens, romaine lettuce, and endive. Each gorilla consumed ten pounds of vegetable matter each day. In addition, they received fruit and flaxseeds scattered throughout the enclosure to encourage foraging. The result of this dramatic shift in diet was a sixty-five-pound weight loss, taking the gorillas from 450 to a leaner 385 pounds, comparable to the weight of an active wild gorilla. The new high-fiber, low-sugar diet also led to a cessation of R&R.

The success of this diet regime with gorillas and with people has led to a formula known as the Omni diet, where 70 percent of the foods consumed are from whole plants and the remainder from high-quality, lean protein. Five years after the changes were instituted, both gorillas were healthy and active. At the time that I published my book *Zoo Man* (Maple, 1995), Willie B. weighed more than five hundred pounds. His diet at that time was comprised of many items that would not be acceptable today. For example, he was given raisins when he could have received lower-calorie grapes. Too much dairy affects R&R, and Willie received three quarts of nonfat milk daily. One pound of high-protein monkey chow is a processed food. On the good side of his diet was a provision of apples, oranges, cabbage, and plenty of browse such as bamboo, banana leaves, willow, and scattered sunflower seeds to encourage foraging.

In the old days, zookeepers occasionally brought him treats such as the famed corn bread obtained from Mrs. Hull's local Victorian boarding house in Grant Park. Willie loved it, but it had to be reserved as an occasional treat, not a feature of his daily diet. Once Willie was surrounded by little offspring, it forced him to be more active in response to their persistent play. He was clearly the most interesting living thing in their purview.

With so many forest plants available for consumption by gorillas in the wild, some of them may be the panacea for a healthy heart. One species, *Afromomum melegueta* (grains of paradise), contains a powerful antibacterial, antiviral, antifungal, and anti-inflammatory compound. Adding this plant to their diet in captivity would be a wise investment in the future of zoo gorillas. *Afromomum* provides 80 to 90 percent of the diet for wild western lowland gorillas. It is one of the most common plants in the lowland swamps they occupy. For gorillas, the plant is a natural drug that is as much preventive medicine as it is food. Currently, there are eight North American zoos that are experimenting with the use of this plant as food for gorillas (T. Stoinski, personal communication). *Afromomum* has potential uses in human medicine as well, another good reason for humanity to protect our planet's storehouse of biodiversity. The production of synthetic medicine in the laboratory should never replace chemical prospecting in forests and aquatic environments.

With so many male gorillas dying from heart disease in their twenties, we dodged a bullet when Willie B. lived to be forty. If we had lost him in his prime, his short life would not have been as sweet. I wonder if we could have imagined such a great zoo in Grant Park without Willie B. He was the inspiration for our aspirations. Fund-raising executives like to say, "people give money to people." In other words, the person who asks for the gift is often more important than the institution he or she represents. In our case, people in Atlanta eagerly gave money to Willie B. His cause was compelling because they had grown up with him and wanted to see improvements in his quality of life.

When a zoo gorilla dies, the organs valuable to science and medicine are typically shared with specialists in medical schools throughout the nation so we can learn more about their health and share our knowledge with other zoos. Even their brains are removed for study, as older apes appear to be susceptible to Alzheimer's disease (Edler et al., 2017; Perez et al., 2016). We value all of our animals in the zoo, and we grieve when we lose them. By law, the bodily parts such as bones and fur of endangered species must be cremated.

Years ago, animals were routinely buried on zoo grounds. We know the gravesites of the first two Atlanta elephants that died at the zoo and the gravesite of the first Willie B. We have to be careful with these remains because there is an active trade in wildlife parts, including lion and tiger skulls, bones, feet, and fur. Zoos don't want to contribute to this illegal activity. In fact, our association has lobbied against the trade, which is centered in South Africa. Trophy hunting in Africa created an active market for wildlife products. In 1978, the government of Kenya banned hunting for trophies and stopped the sale of wildlife products. When *Gorilla Behavior* was published, we were aware of the illegal market for gorilla skulls, hands, and feet.

Today's bushmeat trade has survived the scrutiny of authorities who monitor trade with the goal of ending it. When I served as president of AZA in 1999, one of my priorities was to end the bushmeat trade, but despite the concern of our members and our efforts to encourage government action to combat it, it continues to be one of the most difficult conservation challenges in Africa and Asia. One way to end demand for these products is to advocate an end to the markets and to shame those who patronize them. Television and other media advocacy and museum materials and graphics in our zoos have been informative but not completely effective so far. We are building awareness, but we are not stopping the criminal behavior that endangers gorillas and other species prized for bushmeat in African markets. This is an issue that should concern the American government because trade in bushmeat and wildlife products is operated by the same criminal cartels that traffic in human children and illegal drugs.

Apparently, the motivation to consume and market bushmeat is so strong that local people will risk exposure to deadly diseases such as Ebola. The economic driver of the bushmeat trade is region-wide deficits in protein consumption. People need protein, and there is great demand for it whatever the source. The trade has also become an important source of income for impoverished people. Although greater awareness of the connection of bushmeat to Ebola has led to reductions in bushmeat consumption, it has not been eliminated from the diets of local people. A forthcoming book, *Killing, Capture, Trade and Ape Conservation* (Cambridge) will provide greater detail on the issues that must be confronted.

For those of us who love them, it is tragic when any gorilla dies, but a silverback's death is particularly disturbing. For dedicated field biologists such as Dian Fossey, the brutality of poachers is nothing less than murder. In the zoo, the animals may die quietly, but it is always painful and difficult to accept. Silverbacks are strong and formidable and yet so vulnerable to the cruelty of the desperate men who hunt them.

Chapter 8

APE INTELLECT AND PERSONALITY

Gorillas are very similar to humans in their intellect and personality. Both constructs can be objectively measured in human and beast. Guests who wanted to see Willie B. inevitably asked the question, "How smart is he?" People are equally curious about the strength and the intelligence of gorillas. And they wonder how gorilla personalilty compares to ours. Penny Patterson spent a lifetime with the gorilla Koko, and she was awestruck by the animal's innate communicative skills. Even a short visit with Koko, as I have experienced, requires an adjustment in our thinking about their limitations. Unfortunaely, Koko was studied in a highly subjective social paradigm and it is difficult to separate fact from fiction. I can easily conclude, however, that Koko, like Chantek the orangutan, was an extraordinary animal. I would forgive anyone who concluded she was "almost human".

During my time in Atlanta, as a professor of psychology, and later as the reform director of the zoo, we had every opportunity to carry out a formal study of Willie B.'s intellect. However, as a singleton living in isolation, he didn't seem like a good candidate to generalize to other gorillas. Cognitive research on apes was concentrated on laboratory animals, and priority was given to studies of language or language-like processes. Chimpanzees were more available to scientists who were in close contact with famed subjects, such as the Gardners' chimpanzee Washoe, and Duane Rumbaugh's Lana, the latter a capable young chimp that learned a computer-based language known as Yerkish.

FIGURE 8-2. CONGO EXAMINES HER MIRROR IMAGE (YERKES, 1927).

The first gorilla subjected to communication testing was Koko, born at the San Francisco Zoo and loaned to Penny Patterson, a graduate student at Stanford University. Some of my colleagues believe you cannot study their mental capacity unless you raise them and live with them. Early language studies were conducted on chimpanzees raised in the homes of the investigators. Yerkes himself was in direct contact with some of his subjects, but he prioritized objectivity as it was practiced by trained experimental psychologists at the time. Looking back, I regret we didn't take a greater interest in Willie B.'s problem-solving ability. From studies of their close relatives, chimpanzees, it is clear that all great apes are highly intelligent. The only other species that may equal them are cetaceans.

Robert Yerkes was active in the field of comparative psychology, and he studied a variety of animals early in his career. He and others in this field sought to study great apes and other nonhuman primates, but there weren't many of them available. Further, they have always been a challenge to manage in captive settings. They require more space, Figure 8-2. Congo examines her mirror image (Yerkes, 1927). and they can be aggressive. Rodents and pigeons were more convenient, so they dominate the literature of experimental psychology.

Fortunately, there are large populations of primates available today, in the nation's seven primate research centers and in zoological parks. Atlanta has been blessed with a zoo, an NIH-supported primate center, and a number of primate labs based at our colleges and universities, and a number of highly rated primate labs based at our colleges and center, and a number of primate labs based at our colleges and universities. Another location where primate research is enabled by a large subject population is Chicago, Illinois. Case studies with small numbers of subjects are still being published, but institutions with large collections of monkeys and apes can gather more data efficiently.

Professor Yerkes' study of the female gorilla Congo (Figure 8-2) was published in a monograph that set a new standard for comparative psychology (Yerkes, 1927). His study took several years to complete as he had to travel from New Haven, Connecticut, to Sarasota, Florida, where Congo was relocated after her sale to the Ringling Brothers circus.

One of the tests Yerkes conducted was the mirror image test. He wanted to see if Congo could recognize herself in the mirror, but she persisted in looking behind the mirror and behaving as if it was another animal peering back at her. Her failure to respond appropriately convinced Yerkes that gorillas were inferior to common chimpanzees (*Pan troglodytes*) in their capacity to learn. Chimpanzees, in contrast, used a mirror to examine their teeth and explore other body parts, a useful tool in a zoo or laboratory setting. The response to mirrors became a controversy in the latter years of the twentieth century. Gallup (1970) thoroughly investigated the mirror-image response in chimpanzees and later constructed a theory of mind based on observations of monkeys and apes (Gallup, 1982). Gallup and Anderson (2011) confirmed earlier findings and concluded that only great apes and human beings recognize themselves in mirrors.

Although the phenomenon has not been unequivocally demonstrated in other species, there are some dissenters (de Waal et al., 2005; Rajala et al., 2010). Plotnik, de Waal, and Reiss (2006) documented the mirror-image response in three Asian elephants at the Bronx Zoo. Because these outlier findings pop up frequently with other species, it is important that they be replicated. As for apes, Yerkes was not wrong about gorillas, for other gorillas have struggled to recognize themselves in mirrors (Posada and Collel, 2007). It may be a premature conclusion, but gorillas are widely perceived as less capable than orangutans and chimpanzees. A factor that may interfere with the mirror-image response is the gorilla's innate aversion to a conspecific's gaze. The fixed stare in gorillas is threatening. This is why observers in Africa and visitors to the zoo are advised not to stare at them.

Early in his career, Yerkes had observed many common chimpanzees at the *Quinta Palantino* sanctuary operated by Madame Rosalia Abreu in Cuba (Yerkes, 1925), and he subsequently raised two young chimpanzees himself at his family farm in New Hampshire, but he had carried out formal studies of just one female gorilla (Congo) and one male orangutan (Julius) in the private collection of his former student G. V. Hamilton, a psychiatrist residing on a spacious private estate in Montecito, California. In addition to his psychiatric duties, Dr. Hamilton dabbled in primate psychology (e.g. Maple, 1979b), continuing his correspondence with his former mentor.

When the Abreu colony was translocated to Orange Park, Florida, in 1930, the Yale-affiliated facility acquired a significant number of subjects to study. Scientists who worked at the Orange Park facility explored all aspects of anthropoid life, including mentality, sociality, and ape physiology.

The comparative study of mental capacity was advanced by Yerkes' own interests and native curiosity. As a graduate student at Harvard, Yerkes made the case for a grand, national primate research center (Yerkes, 1916), and he lived long enough to see it accomplished. It was renamed for him prior to his death in 1958 and relocated to Atlanta in 1968. The primate center acquired a small collection of young gorillas and orangutans during its formative years in Atlanta. Some of these animals were loaned to Zoo Atlanta in 1988. Later, Emory University confirmed that the loan would become a gift. A vote of confidence in the zoo, Emory's contribution is one of the most valuable gifts of endangered wildlife in the history of zoos.

Zoo Atlanta has also become a center for cognitive research. A Tech graduate student, Ursula Anderson, examined the ability of gorillas and orangutans at the zoo to select the larger of two quantities. Gorillas performed as well as orangutans and chimpanzees in previous studies (Anderson et al., 2005; Anderson et al., 2007). However, when age is a variable, older gorillas and orangutans were less accurate and slower than younger subjects. Spatial memory studies have also been conducted with a diversity of species, including giant pandas (Tarou et al., 2004; Perdue et al., 2009). Many of the recent cognitive studies conducted with Zoo Atlanta primate subjects are collaborations with outside scientists. For example, Gazes et al. (2017) examined spatial representation of magnitude in gorillas and orangutans, whereby they can select the larger and the smaller quantities of stimuli presented for testing. Both gorilla and orangutan subjects exhibited evidence of spatial representation of magnitude, suggesting that this ability is phylogenetically ancient.

Gorillas have been a conservation priority for more than fifty years. The IUCN, WWF, WCS, AWF, and DFGFI have all invested in protecting gorillas in Africa. Oddly, the attention of conservation organizations has not generated more behavioral research. This may be why they have lagged behind chimpanzees and gorillas in their performance of mental tasks. With more research, I believe we will discover new methods to generate better results. One device that shows promise with gorillas is the puzzle maze developed at the Bristol Zoo and Gardens in the United Kingdom.

This simple device kept the subjects engaged. By using their fingers instead of a tool, they were successful in solving the problem (Clark et al., 2019).

PONGID PERSONALITY

Like the construct "mind," we recognize that "personality" is a hypothetical construct that helps us understand an important attribute of our biology. Does personality apply to great apes? At the time that Mike Hoff and I published our book on gorillas, little was known about personality in animals. However, due to the success of behavioral laboratories at UC Berkeley and at the University of Texas, the list of personality studies is growing by leaps and bounds (Bensky et al., 2013; Freeman and Gosling, 2010; Gosling, 1998; King and Figueredo, 1997).

Harlow and his colleagues published an early study of personality in rhesus monkeys (Chamove et al., 1972), using the same factor analytic techniques applied in studies of human personality. They identified three main factors in this species: fearful, hostile, and affectionate. An article by Weiss et al. (2014) reported on an 18-year longitudinal study of personality predictors of survival in a huge sample of 283 lowland gorillas. The investigators demonstrated that extraversion was the only factor associated with longer survival. There was no effect with the other dimensions of dominance, neuroticism, and agreeableness. How this variable contributes to longevity is not currently known, but it seems to be equally powerful when compared to variations in demographic or husbandry history. Clearly, this is an issue that deserves additional study. There is little doubt that animals have distinct personalities that can be studied by psychologists.

In 1978, I began a pilot study of great ape personality at the Yerkes National Primate Research Center in collaboration with an Emory undergraduate, Ron Schonwetter. We examined the response of chimpanzees, gorillas, and orangutans to the simple presentation of food when the animals were fed by staff each day. I used the word "temperament" to describe the repertoire of expression that we observed. Much like the findings of Yerkes and Yerkes (1929), we found that chimpanzees were the most expressive in the presence of food. Gorillas and orangutans were more stoic, with fewer vocalizations and emotional displays. Compared to their close relatives, gorillas and orangs, chimpanzees do not suffer captivity gladly. For this reason, many zoos no longer exhibit them, preferring to offer quieter calmer species to the public. Chimpanzees also invite criticism as people perceive them as unhappy, even angry. Another issue is the fact that chimpanzees in groups have fatally injured each other, and this too calls attention to the deficiencies of their situation. In 2012, a male chimpanzee killed an infant at the Los Angeles Zoo. This and other documented acts of aggression by chimpanzees are problematic for successful exhibition in a zoo. In nature, chimpanzees live in large groups, whereas gorillas live in smaller families led by a dominant male, and orangutans are relatively solitary by comparison. Curators agree that aggression is a much bigger problem with common chimpanzees. Research on wild and captive chimpanzees led one group of scientists to conclude that chimpanzees are naturally violent (Wilson et al., 2014). By contrast, the closely related bonobo is essentially nonviolent. For example, Garai et al (2016) used questionnaire ratings and behavioral observations to examine factors influencing personality in 16 wild bonobos at Wamba in the Democratic Republic of Congo. The investigators confirmed that there was no clear dominance factor in this subject pool, and this finding is consistent with the more egalitarian structure of bonobo society. In addition, there was generally lower levels of aggression in bonobos as other studies have documented (Kano, 1992; Parish and de Waal, 2000).

The other side of this argument is the clear need to increase the Species Survival Plan (SSP) population of chimpanzees and to recruit support for chimpanzee field conservation. For many reasons, chimpanzees have not been the first choice for the exhibition of apes, so it may take a comprehensive review of the issues to make the case for their renewal. There are some fine chimpanzee exhibits in the United States and in Europe, and more published research on chimpanzees than on the other great apes. Because there is so much known about chimpanzees, zoos may prefer to commission research on the lesser-known gorillas and orangutans.

Naturalistic zoo design usually mitigates aggression, but it won't eliminate it. If we had been stronger financially in 1988, I would not have hesitated to recommend an exhibit of chimpanzees. For many years, the city zoo had exhibited a pair of chimpanzees, but their cage was barren and bleak. The opportunity to provide solutions to control their emotional makeup was an interesting design dilemma. As a comparative psychologist, I was also intrigued by the prospect of exhibiting three species of apes in contiguous facilities. Not many zoos have the resources to do this.

In the end, our design team made the decision to exhibit two taxa representing apes from Africa and apes from Asia. Ultimately, our gorilla exhibit was widely recognized as the best in the world. Our orangutan exhibit was not as advanced, but it had many unique features, such as our commitment to verticality. We missed other opportunities to equal the quality of the gorilla exhibit due to the limits of our budget. The most salient feature of the exhibit was the artificial tree that encouraged orangutans to climb to a height of fifty-four feet. When an animal ascended to the very top of this tree, it was visible to all of our visitors throughout the park.

Other zoos have surpassed our standard in providing innovative arboreal simulations for orangutans, but no zoo has built a better gorilla exhibit. Recently, Zoo Atlanta installed computerized cognitive workstations so orangutans and gorillas can be offered enrichment and studied. For Zoo Atlanta's achievements in the exhibition, study, and conservation of great apes, it was recently honored with AZA's prestigious Edward H. Bean Award.

PERSONALITY AND MANAGEMENT

An important early study of gorilla personality was conducted for his doctoral dissertation by Ken Gold (Gold and Maple, 1994). Gold was interested in understanding how gorilla personality could predict zoo management outcomes. To assess the power of this construct, he developed the Gorilla Behavior Index (GBI). Prior to his quantitative approach, gorillas were managed almost at random, with subjective evaluations rather than evidence-based data determining the outcomes. Throughout my service years on the Gorilla SSP, I regularly consulted with Ken, who knew every one of the gorillas in the North American SSP population. Another example of the value of students, Ken Gold was a remarkable resource. For several years, he worked for the Gorilla Foundation in California. When the resident gorilla Koko died, he coauthored a very astute obituary published in the *American Journal of Primatology* (Gold and Watson, 2018).

On his expedition to capture specimens for museums, Carl Akeley also commented on the personality of gorillas. The diaries and records of Akeley have been examined in detail by his biographer Jay Kirk (2010). Kirk found evidence that Akeley felt guilty about the gorillas he killed for taxidermy. His feelings were based on his recognition that there was something human about the gorilla. As Kirk reported:

> This old ape had had its own dilemmas. It made him feel
> like a murderer, not just because in a distorted way it looked
> humanish—but because, unlike a zebra or hippopotamus,
> it had that vague quality of personality. Zebras had fierce
> spirit, but they did not have individual character.

Congo was one of the first gorillas to be evaluated for her personality. Yerkes made many astute observations about Congo's mild temperament. She was far less emotional than chimpanzees Yerkes had studied, but she also exhibited less curiosity about her environment. This reticence made her less valuable as a subject for studying intelligence. She seemed to handle stress without overt consequences, but she died shortly after her arrival at the circus, indicating the change of venue may have been too demanding. Montgomery (2009) opined that Congo died of loneliness.

Like Congo, Willie B. was an affable ape who clearly had a tolerance for high stress. Most of the time, he expressed a relaxed façade with only subtle signs of tension (when he saw me, for example!). The species-typical gorilla tense face was a feature that made him such an excellent subject for photography. A talented local photographer, Joe Sebo, produced hundreds of images of Willie B., but as far as I know, he never organized them into a book. I hope his family one day recognizes the value of this treasure trove of primate history. Joe's photographs and Mike Luckovich's caricatures of

Willie B. are displayed in my office with the pride I feel for the drawings of my own children.

Steklis and his associates have examined personality variables in wild mountain gorillas (Eckhardt et al, 2015). The investigators discovered four factors in this sample of 116 gorillas: dominance, openness, sociability, and proto-agreeableness. Those who scored higher in the latter category were friendly, emotionally stable, and content. This description best fits Willie B's temperament, but all silverbacks are capable of greater dominance when it is required.

Willie B. posters sold well at our gift shop and occupied the walls of many of Atlanta's finest corporate and educational leaders. Fortunately, his personality is revealed in many of these images. Many distinguished artists captured his image in paintings, some hanging in the zoo in public view. A particularly striking portrait by the Japanese painter Chisato Abe can be seen in the Conservation Action Resource Center. Another portrait of hers is illustrated on the cover of this book. She was so moved by his magnificence that she painted the original portrait gratis and had it sent to us in Atlanta. His personality made him likable to other gorillas and to millions of zoo visitors, and an attractive model for artists and illustrators trying to capture his mood and his spirit.

Some of the best paintings were donated to the zoo for the Beastly Feast auction. They always fetched a handsome price, so his image continues to be a money maker for the zoo. We also issued a collection of "baseball" cards with the image and vital statistics for each one of our gorillas. Today we regard Willie B. as a classic animal model of resilience. His recovery to live as a normal, social silverback was indeed a miracle.

EMPATHY AND CONSERVATION

As our citizens were motivated to improve his quality of life, we can hope that revitalized zoological parks will play an important role in conserving wild gorillas and their fragile habitats. The previously mentioned murders of African park rangers by poachers in recent years illustrates both the fragility and the threats to the existence of wild gorillas. Gorillas in the zoo should be presented to remind us that they are highly vulnerable in the wild, and must be protected by the people who value them.

In the latest issue of AZA *Connect*, the offical magazine of the Association of Zoos and Aquariums, the status of wild chimpanzee populations is discussed in some detail (Collins, 2021). Their growing importance as a conservation priority of the AZA SAFE (Saving Animals from Extention) program is a good reason for zoos to consider exhibiting them. SAFE is actively monitoring and protecting all four recognized subspecies of chimpanzees: western, Nigeria-Cameroon, central, and eastern. The goals of this ambitious program are to increase cooperation among AZA and other conservation organizations, combat chimpanzee population decline, increase public stakeholder engagement, build awareness of chimpanzee conservation efforts, and create additional funding. All chimpanzees in Africa are threatened by poaching, habitat loss, and outbreaks of infectious disease.

A United Nations conservation organization recently commented on the need to protect chimpanzee culture. The UN's Convention on the Conservation of Migratory Species (CMS) has agreed to protect a chimpanzee nut-cracking culture unique to populations in Guinea, Sierra Leone, Liberia, and the Ivory Coast. The animals use stones and pieces of wood as hammers and anvils to open nuts. CMS authorities acknowledged the need to promote this phenomenon, asserting that: "Discoveries about animal culture can be fascinating to the public at large, shaping their perceptions of the nature of the animals concerned and hence their value." Field studies of chimpanzees continue to discover details about the cognitive capacity of this species. When we have studied gorillas and orangutans with the commitment we've shown to chimpanzees, we will surely discover more evidence of their complexity and their culture. Since we can learn from the great apes only if they survive, protecting populations and ecosystems should be our first priority.

Culture is likely to be evident in many other big-brained, social animals including elephants, dolphins, and whales. We know that traditions are important in the llife history of Japanese macaques that have been observed for decades, so many monkey species lead complex lives in the wild. It is only a matter of time before we discover how widespread culture is in the animal world. The evolution of human culture begins with its origins in populations of nonhuman species.

Chapter 9

GROUP LIFE, COURTSHIP, FATHERHOOD

FIGURE 9-1. BABY MOUNTAIN GORILLA BONNE ANNE (J. D. FOWLER).

In the wild, all gorillas live in social groups, both heterosexual family groups and single-sex bachelor groups in which aspiring males look to form a harem by recruiting females from established groups. The family is usually led by a dominant silverback who fiercely defends the group when danger appears. There are some groups that tolerate more than one adult silverback, although it is not the norm. When we designed the Ford African Rain Forest exhibit, we envisioned a setting where dominant males would respond to other silverbacks, creating perceived competition among them. Zoos had a poor record of breeding gorillas, so we thought we could motivate them with this arrangement of contiguous territories. Since they bred almost immediately, we can't be sure that our plan didn't work, but there were few indicators that they noticed the other males. Given the power of the gorilla stare, perhaps they were averting their gaze to avoid conflict with their neighbors.

Once offspring arrived, males exhibited interest in them. The mothers of these babies were superior parents because of the presence of the male. Eventually, babies began to venture out on their own to play with their peers or approach the adult male. Silverbacks attract the attention of young gorillas. Some silverbacks reciprocate with vigorous play. When Willie B. sired offspring at the zoo, he proved to be a friendly, playful father. Although it is unusual for silverbacks to initiate play, they are extremely tolerant of exuberant contact by their offspring. In Jacksonville, my zoo colleagues frequently observed rough and tumble play between the adult male Rumpel and his active male offspring, George (D. Maloney, personal communication). Little apes love to crawl over the bodies of their fathers. The boldest of them will even take food out of the mouths of the silverback.

Paternalistic behavior was the last of Harlow's affectional systems to be investigated. A few of these studies focused on gorillas. Tilford and Nadler (1978) found that captive adult male lowland gorillas expressed a greater interest in immatures than is typically seen in wild mountain gorillas. Male gorillas in research or zoo settings may be a useful population for the discovery of the full range of paternal behaviors. For example, in captive settings, male gorillas occasionally kidnap offspring and run away with them until their mother retrieves them. One factor that may explain the differences in captive and wild subjects is the amount of time available for interacting with offspring. Wild gorillas are just too busy foraging for food. In a larger sample of zoo gorillas, Enciso et al. (1999) found that infants were the primary initiators of contact with males. In this study, consistent with wild data, silverbacks exhibited little interest in the offspring. However, males in the zoo were more responsive to related kin, indicating agreement with a kin selection model.

Although Willie B. did not exhibit stereotyped behaviors or indulge in R&R or coprophagia, we expected him to be socially incompetent. However, his deficiencies were correctable. We just had to find a way to approach his resocialization that was safe. After considerable debate, we decided to introduce Willie to a young female, Kinyani. She was chosen because Harlow had some success with therapist monkeys that were less threatening to his isolate subjects. To diffuse any aggression, we cautiously introduced her along with another, more experienced female.

It is standard practice in zoos to introduce animals behind barriers at first, giving them a chance to see and smell the stranger. This process is called "howdying." When the barriers were removed, Kinyani avoided the big silverback, but her companion, Katoomba, provided his first contact with another gorilla since he left Africa. She slapped him on the face and then retreated. He seemed confused, but after a few days together, he began to court the lovely Kinyani. It took several months before I was called by keeper Charles Horton to witness his first successful copulation. It was a splendid day, the first day of the rest of his social life, and one of the best days of my career. The media interest in this courtship process had the advantage that it kept people guessing about the outcome. Print and media reporters hounded our public relations department for inside information about the progress of their courtship, and a series of stories appeared in the *Atlanta Journal-Constitution* charting the progress of their very public relationship.

Although Willie B. seemed to enjoy copulating, he was sometimes confused by an abundance of opportunities. I observed him on one occasion with a cabbage in one hand when Kinyani backed into him to copulate. What followed was a comical sexual thrust, then a bite of the cabbage, thrusting, then eating. He managed to multitask on this and many other occasions as he gained experience. Willie B. turned out to be a normal gorilla after all, but the baby steps he took were comical at times. Willie lacked social experience, but he made up for it with enthusiasm.

With these early sexual encounters documented, he had passed the threshold for a social and a sexual silverback. We could now dare to think about introducing him to a harem of females with the hope he would reproduce and learn to be a father. Although he produced no offspring when he lived with Katoomba and Kinyani, the introduction of Choomba, an experienced breeder, resulted in an infant born in 1994. Willie B. sired five offspring from 1994 to 1999: Kudzoo, Olympia, Sukari, Kidogo, and Lulu. This was important since the gorilla SSP had identified Willie B. as a high priority for breeding. His genes were now accessible to the captive population.

Since the Ford African Rain Forest exhibit opened in 1988, twenty-four gorillas have been born at Zoo Atlanta, and only one was not raised by its biological mother, an extraordinary record. The one exception, Jasiri, was an unusual case study. His mother Katoomba abandoned him, and he had to be retrieved by the zookeepers. Because he had a fractured arm, he required human care, as our vets feared further injury from the other, curious apes. Removing him from the group was a last but necessary resort. Soon thereafter, our staff successfully introduced him to Paki, an experienced mother who was not carrying an infant at the time. She readily responded to Jasiri and raised him as if he was her own. Because Paki was not producing milk, the staff trained her to present Jasiri for feeding from the keepers who supplied a bottle under careful supervision.

This was another notable success story for the Zoo Atlanta keeper team (Warner, 1998), and testimony to the skilled staff we were building. A key player in this process was Charles Horton, who eventually became our first curator of primates. He was widely known as Willie B.'s best friend. I hope Charles puts together his thoughts about his unique relationship with Willie B. and some day writes his own book about him. When Charles got married, he arranged for the ceremony to take place just outside Willie B.'s outdoor habitat. It could be argued that this was his way of honoring Willie as his "best man." Our socialization process depended on the strong social bonds between Willie B. and Charles. We all envied his unique friendship.

Terry L. Maple

THE LEGACY OF H.F. HARLOW

Professor Harlow and his students worked for decades experimenting with psychopathology induced by social deprivation, while attempting to provide rehabilitative socialization to achieve improvements. I spent enough time in the company of deprived monkeys that I recognized the symptoms whenever they appeared in primates at the many zoos I visited. In fact, California zoos were populated with a plethora of crazy monkeys and apes produced by caregivers who didn't understand how to create normally socialized animals. Once zoo professionals began to pay attention to the psychological literature, zoos were able to engineer better conditions for optimal rearing and social development.

Most of what we know about the effects of social deprivation is based on laboratory studies of rhesus monkeys, but we have some ape data to add to the equation. In an important publication, Beck and Power (1988) offered their recommendations to zoo managers who were concerned about how to inoculate gorillas against deprivation syndrome. Accordingly, they concluded:

> Reproductive failure is not due solely to lack of access to potential mates or to physiological abnormalities. Rather we have shown that many reproductively unsuccessful adults, both wild born and captive born, exhibit behavioral deficits . . . deprivation is a significant factor in many cases of reproductive failure (p. 348).

Others have pondered the efficacy of therapeutic interventions for deprived gorillas. Abello et al. (2011) suggested that sexually experienced gorillas might be able to help hand-reared gorillas to breed. In a study published in the *International Zoo Yearbook*, the investigators reviewed a European population of 117 hand-reared gorillas. From a survey, they suggested that females should be introduced into socially competent groups where breeding can be observed. Males would be evaluated from their exposure to socially competent groups and adult females with a history

94

of breeding. The investigators discovered that females that bred had been exposed to breeding by others. Males learned to copulate by observing experienced animals and also by interacting through socio-sexual play bouts with peers and older animals.

FIGURE 9-1. WILLIE B. COPULATES WITH KINYANI.

These findings support my long-held view that sexual behavior was not learned by watching alone; it required some degree of active participation. Arousal can be achieved by either visual or tactual stimuli. Attempts to arouse disinterested gorillas by the presentation of films of gorillas has been attempted, but it has never been successful, suggesting that the acquisition of sexual skills requires exposure to a complexity of variables. This is why gorillas raised by human caregivers require rough and tumble play with people or conspecific peers.

Gorillas and other apes were socially deprived due to our ignorance as exhibitors. Old-school zoo directors did not value the family as an important variable in a gorilla's life at the zoo. We learned about their needs by observing them over their lifetimes. Changes in management and husbandry functioned as natural experiments and tested what could be done to improve their lives. Harlow's work with Rhesus monkeys was largely experimental. He created isolate and socially deprived monkeys in order to exhaustively study how these conditions were produced. Animal rights organizations criticized him for the suffering of his subjects, but I have always appreciated the fact that Harlow's exhaustive experimentation provided the framework for understanding deprivation effects and gave curators and veterinarians a basis for correcting it. Thanks to Harlow and his students, there is no good reason to produce any more isolate apes but we should study those subjects that have inadvertently suffered isolation.

FIGURE 9-2. WILLIE B. TOLERATES TODDLER WHILE
FEEDING. (COURTESY ZOO ATLANTA)

THE YERKES TRANSACTION

The Atlanta situation was as good as it gets. We received a small population of adult males and females on loan from the Yerkes National Primate Research Center. The original harem groups translocated to the zoo in 1988 were organized into three groups. *Group 1:* Rann, Choomba, Katoomba, Shamba; *Group 2:* Ozoum, Paki, Machi, Kuchi, Kinyani; *Group 3:* Calabar, Oko, Ndiyo, Radi. With a total of fourteen gorillas including Willie B., we knew we had assembled sufficient numbers to socialize them and successfully breed them. The big question was Willie B.'s social potential, or as a Ford public relations pundit wondered, "Will he, or won't he?" Thankfully, he fulfilled his promise and became a successful breeder and parent. After all these years with peers of his own kind, he would finally become the measure of a genuine silverback.

Once my students and our key staff began to focus on documenting socialization deficits in great apes, we were able to share our findings with other institutions. The lead author of our first published account of Willie B.'s socialization was Curator of Mammals Sam Winslow. It appeared in the *International Zoo Yearbook* (Winslow et al., 1992). A decade later, Burks and colleagues (2001) analyzed data from the four-step socialization process of Ivan, a gorilla with a similar background to Willie B. One important difference in the developmental history of these two gorillas was that Willie B. spent most of his time alone, whereas Ivan was raised as if he were a sibling in the home of his human family. Of course, we did not control all of the life experience variables for either animal, so our historical accounts were imperfect at best.

The sensational media accounts of Willie B.'s story gave hope to every zoo with socially deprived animals. Although animal rights groups were unhappy with the Atlanta Zoo prior to my arrival, they were not focused on Willie B. In Ivan's case, a nonprofit organization known as the Progressive Animal Welfare Society (PAWS) led the fight to free him from his home at the B&I Department Store in Tacoma. For Ivan to have a chance to become a socialized gorilla, we had to go to court. Thankfully, a just decision was rendered, and his translocation to Zoo Atlanta was a story with a happy ending.

One conclusion that can be drawn is the fact that Willie B. and Ivan made progress with carefully managed socialization protocols. With both of these socially deprived animals, there was a tremendous risk of lethal aggression. Thanks to the meticulous, day-to-day exposure to other animals, both Willie B. and Ivan responded to social opportunity and eventually led a normal social life with other gorillas. Willie became comfortable with his gorilla family and surprised all of us by reproducing. Willie B.'s story has been told again and again by journalists and covered by extensive televised historiography (*The Urban Gorilla* by Allison Argo), but there is more to tell. Without a doubt, Willie became an accepted member of his own gorilla family. In every way, he behaved like a normal, dominant silverback.

By contrast, although he accepted the company of other gorillas, Ivan always preferred people. The complete story of Ivan's life has not been written, but a fictional account for children was recently produced by the Walt Disney Company. Representatives of the company called me when they began to produce the film. That courteous gesture motivated me to examine the book and the film. Disney bought the rights to the best-selling book *The One and Only Ivan* by Katherine Applegate (2012). Ivan has a voice in the book and the film. Disney's computer-generated gorilla is based on living gorillas, and Ivan is very realistic. True to aspects of the real story, Ivan is eventually liberated to live in a naturalistic zoo. However, in the film, his habitat is vast, much larger than our habitats in Atlanta. He is depicted smelling and eating flowers and clearly enjoying the feel of green grass. I regard this as an endorsement of modern zoo design. To her credit, Applegate acknowledges Zoo Atlanta's role in rescuing Ivan.

I think Disney hit a home run with this movie because it highlights the difference between hard and soft architecture and the dramatic shift in our management philosophy. Although Ivan is treated well by his human caregivers, he is initially portrayed as a performing animal. In modern zoos, apes are no longer entertainers. Once liberated to a social life at Zoo Atlanta, Ivan's only responsibility was to be himself.

We are flattered that the Walt Disney Company would ultimately pay homage to our work in fact or fiction, but we are still waiting for the full story of Ivan and the noble zoo professionals who freed him to be told. Disney's reputation in conservation and science is well known, so the company has the credibility to produce a family film such as *The One and Only Ivan*. It may appear self-serving, but I must remind my Disney colleagues that it may also be time for a film about the life of Willie B. Without Willie B., there could not have been a true story of Ivan. Willie B. was the model who helped free a generation of isolated male gorillas. It was my pleasure to lead the way for both Willie and Ivan to rejoin the social network of fellow gorillas.

INVESTING IN THE NEXT GENERATION

Several master plans were adopted by the City of Atlanta and the Atlanta Zoological Society before I came on board. I am thankful that they were not built—they were far short of the quality the new zoo visionaries were seeking. The acquisition of gorillas was difficult in those days, and our investment in Willie B.'s future required a large number of gorillas to form breeding groups. After the Ford African Rain Forest exhibit opened, there was great demand for similar facilities, but without sufficient numbers of available gorillas, many zoos decided to exhibit groups of young adult males. At one point, Zoo Atlanta had so many surplus males we had to send them to other facilities. Willie B. Jr./Kidogo spent some of his formative years with his sibling Jasiri at the Dewar Wildlife Trust in North Georgia. These placeholder exhibits anticipated the day when breeding females would be available.

FIGURE 9.3. KIDOGO PLAYS WITH JASIRI AT DEWAR TRUST FACILITY. (S. DEWAR).

The ultimate goal of naturalistic family groups was to have infants raised in a group by their biological mothers. Once a zoo started breeding gorillas, the story of their development became a compelling reason to visit the zoo again and again. Interactions between Willie B. and his offspring were worth the wait. At the peak of his success as a silverback in 1998, Willie's group reached the zenith of its complexity. The group consisted of young gorillas and their mothers, a total of ten animals. Willie was a typical gorilla father, although we did record significant variation in the behavior of other adult males. Willie often surprised us with expressions of his fatherhood. His keepers reported that Willie was the most playful silverback in our collection. Perhaps his long history of playing with his keepers and zoo visitors shaped this behavior and prepared him for fatherhood. He also demonstrated empathy and altruism. Charles Horton sent me a charming account revealing Willie's concern about his kids:

> One memorable incident occurred when Kidogo was playing with one of his sisters, rolled off the edge and fell into the moat. The gorillas, especially his mother Machi, were very upset. Staff responded by calling the gorillas inside as they prepared to rescue Kidogo with a rope. All the gorillas complied but Willie B. There was no way he was going to leave Kidogo in the moat. He lingered near the edge waiting for Kidogo to climb the rope. Once his son was near the top, Willie B. reached out and pulled him into the habitat. Wow!

Charles also observed frequent play between Willie B. and Kudzoo. She chased him indoors and outdoors, and he sometimes initiated the chase. He could catch her indoors, but she was faster outdoors. His interest in the offspring was really quite remarkable.

THE GOOD, THE BAD, AND THE UGLY

Zoos that do not try to breed endangered animals run the risk that the community will begin to see the zoo as an exploiter of wildlife. This can also happen when a zoo becomes too entertainment oriented. Of the four purposes of zoological parks—conservation, education, entertainment, and science—entertainment should be the last priority. When zoos abandon their nobler purpose, they drift to an operating standard characteristic of roadside attractions. This is the dark side of exhibition and should be resisted.

There is an abundance of substandard attractions in the state of Florida, but only a handful of accredited zoos and aquariums that meet the highest operating and ethical standards of the Association of Zoos and Aquariums. However, because of their large numbers, we still have to worry about roadside attractions. Their poor execution of facility design and ethical lapses are a stain on the entire industry of animal exhibition, so we must be careful to differentiate between accredited zoos and unaccredited attractions. While some of my colleagues believe we can mentor roadsides into compliance with our standards, I have my doubts. We can only educate our visitors, members, and friends that they should not patronize such institutions.

If the media did their job, these places would be exposed and eventually shut down due to organized public condemnation. We worked too hard to revitalize and reform zoos in Atlanta, New Orleans, and other major cities to witness suffering by animals still living in truly horrid conditions. Not every town and city deserves a zoo. There is a major league of zoos that requires human and financial resources that are equal to the task of high-quality exhibition. Theme parks that have risen to the occasion by superior exhibition and a commitment to quality include Busch Gardens in Tampa, Florida, and Disney's Animal Kingdom in Orlando (Maple and Mallavarapu, 2006). We should aim high when we plan any new zoos and aquariums. We can learn from theme parks, but we should not emulate them.

Chapter 10

MARKETING SILVERBACKS

FIGURE 10-1. WILLIE B. WAS THE POSTER BOY FOR RESILIENCE.

Willie B.'s visage was a formidable fund-raising tool. We never tried to offer him to promote products, but if we had, I have no doubt he would have become one of the most successful brands in the world. Today we have Gorilla Glue and a local soccer club branded as the Silverbacks, but the original Willie B. has no equal in the annals of marketing. Zoo Atlanta produced posters, T-shirts, and coffee cups with his image, and occasionally hired artists to produce caricatures of his face and his robust body. *Atlanta Journal-Constitution* cartoonist Mike Luckovich was among the best of those who drew Willie B. to satirize current events. Often, Willie's cartoon illustrated events at the zoo. Speaking to his adoring public through human interpreters, Willie B. expressed opinions about everything.

FORD'S HEROIC INTERVENTION

The Ford Motor Company was intrigued by the Willie B. story when they first began to look for opportunities to raise their profile in Atlanta. They were brought to the negotiating table by our friend, Jan Pringle of Pringle, Dixon, Pringle, a local public relations company. Ford's first financial commitment enabled the zoo to hire world-class architects Coe & Lee to design the world's best gorilla exhibit in Atlanta. At the same time, Ford agreed to underwrite ten days of travel in Africa, where our team of curators, educators, and designers studied gorilla habitat and local architecture. Our adventure was produced by local television station WSB/ Channel Two, with their production expenses underwritten by Ford. The prime-time television show *In the Heart of the Jungle* received an Emmy Award for the production and won the audience against all competitors on the night of its showing.

To generate additional publicity about the partnership, Ford also provided funding for a sophisticated model of the rain forest exhibit suitable for travel exhibits throughout the city, and they gave us two Ford vehicles to brand for our education outreach programs. Their most important gift to the zoo was their engagement as sponsors of the zoo's annual black-tie dinner, known as "The Beastly Feast." This unique marketing and philanthropic partnership has continued to this day, now thirty-five years and counting. I know of no other example of such an enduring sponsor in modern zoo history.

As they promised, Ford's involvement has raised millions of dollars, year after year, to support the zoo and its programs. We also delivered on our promise to design a world-class exhibit second to none. Ford's own surveys have demonstrated that the zoo relationship has elevated their profile as a corporate citizen in the city. Stories about their involvement with the zoo appeared in the *New York Times* and in *National Geographic* magazine. The fact that a Dearborn, Michigan, company was so supportive of a zoo in the state of Georgia may seem odd to some, but at the time of their gift, Ford had operated a plant in Atlanta for seventy-five years.

Ford's marketing of the zoo also encouraged other sponsors to step forward. I noted at the time that the zoo and Ford were in the same business; the family business. To affirm my loyalty to the company, I traded my Dodge Caravan for a new Ford Windstar and even today continue to drive Ford vehicles. I was also unwavering in my support for Coca-Cola, even when I visited a Pepsi-funded zoo. My domestic travel was always booked on Atlanta-based Delta Airlines, but international travel sometimes required the selection of other airlines, some of whom sponsored our travel programs.

The most active partner was Swiss Air. This partnership led to our friendship with Zoo Zurich, where I collaborated with curator Christian Schmidt, a former student and protégé of Heini Hediger. Schmidt was instrumental in helping me to set up a video interview with Hediger, now available on YouTube. Schmidt was so impressed with our commitment to marketing that he spent several months in Atlanta learning how we coordinated public relations and marketing in our corporate community. While he learned marketing by working with our team of staff and volunteers, he passed on new ideas from Zoo Zurich that improved our approach to husbandry and enrichment. Schmidt eventually moved to Germany, where he assumed the directorship of Frankfurt Zoo, continuing his lifelong conservation commitments in East Africa.

PRIMATE IMAGES

A few years ago, I noticed an article in the sports pages describing a little-known bowl game, the Boot Hill Bowl, which featured two small college football teams. One of them was located in Pittsburg, Kansas, and they are known as the Gorillas. As a sports fan and an observer of wildlife, I could not recall any other team with a nonhuman primate mascot. There were no Boston Baboons, no Minnesota Macaques, no Louisville Lemurs or Chattanooga Chimpanzees. To put this into perspective, I conducted an informal survey to discover which taxa were the most commonly used for branding. Tigers and bulldogs led the list, with eagles and hawks close behind, but only the gorillas were counted in the primate column.

Given what I knew, it was my special pleasure when I received a call from David Cormack, Robert Glustrom, and John Latham, owners of the new Atlanta soccer franchise. They told me they had been inspired by Willie B.'s story and wanted to honor him in their inaugural season. It was thrilling to learn that they had named their team the Silverbacks. If only Willie B. himself could have understood how much he was loved and respected. The Silverback owners contributed funds to help us with the memorial sculpture of Willie B. and agreed to raise additional money at Silverback games. So I represented Willie B. at the first home game, giving a pep talk to the team, and cheered with the other fans as the Silverbacks gave their best effort. My daughter Sally was playing soccer at the time, so the two of us enjoyed the game together.

I think more teams should look to biodiversity for creative names. This would be one way to free themselves of the negative connotations from team names that exploit indigenous people. In fact, I would urge all college and professional teams to adopt an endangered or threatened species as their mascot and generate funds to protect them. Ted Turner accomplished this when he named his new hockey team the Thrashers, Georgia's state bird. Universities have adopted creative alternatives to their original nicknames.

For example, Stanford University abandoned their "Indian" nickname and became the "Cardinal." In their logo, they inserted a redwood tree, and their funny mascot is a dancing redwood (The Tree) that entertains the fans at sporting venues. Other examples include the UC Irvine Anteaters, the UC Santa Cruz Banana Slugs, and the Imperial Valley Junior College Fighting Avocados. Native Americans might be happier if the Atlanta Braves branded themselves as Aardvarks, Antlions, or Armadillos. If they chose a primate moniker, the Atlanta Anthropoids would be an appropriate choice. Willie B. was a dignified creature, nearly human, but we were not afraid to have fun with his image.

The current "cancel culture" promoted by some political figures is so extreme that schools named for American heroes are being renamed at an alarming rate. If we want to avoid controversy, we should avoid naming institutions after people, no matter how heroic they are at the time of naming. We could use the same approach that I recommend with sports teams. George Washington High School could become Giant Panda High School. For Abraham Lincoln, we might use the namesake Golden Eagle High School. Endangered animals can be honored without offending anyone or any group. I don't agree with the trends in cancel culture, but if it simplifies communication and cooperation, then why not adopt names that elevate the image of endangered animals and places—for example, Okefenokee Alligator High School, or Everglades Egret Elementary?

TRUTH IN ADVERTISING

Occasionally Willie B. was the arbiter in a public service role. American Tourister luggage issued a television ad in which a gorilla (actually a large chimpanzee) tried to tear up one of its best-made suitcases. The company alleged that the product passed the test with flying colors. The zoo was approached by a local television channel investigating truth in advertising to see if Willie B. could confirm the strength and durability of the suitcase. When the suitcase was delivered to our silverback, he promptly tore it in half and used half of the product to scoop water and drink from it. The product looked pretty flimsy in the massive hands of our primate test pilot. The show of force was a big hit on local television, and everybody was talking about it the next day. We didn't agree to this test for money; we simply wanted to create a media buzz.

Willie B. also made international news in 1978 when he responded to the presentation of a new television to replace the set that was stolen from him. At first it was a mystery that drove public sympathy for him—the entire city wondered who could be so cruel as to deprive him of one of his only amenities. It remained a mystery until local police solved the crime and identified the culprit.

AZS public relations chair Patricia Dann organized a citywide publicity blitz to call attention to Willie B.'s plight. Willie was offered dozens of television sets from sympathetic zoo patrons as far away as California. On his behalf, leaders of the Atlanta Zoological Society accepted the donation of a 19-inch color television from Mr. and Mrs. Dick Pierce of Tracy, Tennessee. His new TV was presented during the Christmas season by Mrs. Dann and a man in a gorilla suit, white beard, and red hat, or Santa Gorilla as we called him. Santa Gorilla looked a lot like me. Willie was not amused, but he accepted the gift with a grunt and went about his business. As he watched TV, we watched him, and several media outlets wrote about his television preferences. It was clear that he liked action: football, professional wrestling, etc.

National publicity was generated out of this simple stunt, so Pat Dann was correct in her assessment that this could be a big story. Unfortunately, it didn't generate the public commitment to upgrade the gorilla exhibit that we had hoped for. Willie's plight took another decade of continuous political struggle to deliver the resources to finally free him for his new life in the Ford African Rain Forest. The long suffering Zoological Society and an entire city of volunteers worked diligently for reform. On behalf of Willie B., I salute them all for their patience and their persistence. It was my pleasure to provide the leadership that finally delivered the kind of zoo we could only dream about during the toughest days of our collective struggle. It is difficult to understand how government leaders could have avoided the needs of our city zoo for so long. When private citizens stepped up, however, the city required that they prove themselves ready to govern and to manage. This stand-off took awhile to resolve.

FIGURE 10-2. KIDOGO, AKA WILLIE B. JR. (ZOO ATLANTA).

Little did we know that Willie B. would be so socially successful and that one day his only male offspring Kidogo, aka Willie B. Jr., would inherit his own harem of breeding females. He is the spitting image of his father. Hopefully, there will always be a Willie B. at Zoo Atlanta, at least for the foreseeable future. Thus, the marketing of a charismatic silverback at Zoo Atlanta will continue. Fame can be fleeting, but the Willie B. brand is powerful. In the film *Fierce Creatures*, starring John Cleese, the mythical zoo in the film was modeled on Zoo Atlanta, and Willie B.'s name is mentioned as one of the prominent childhood memories of costar Jamie Lee Curtis.

Willie B.'s story is particularly noteworthy since the lingering uncertainty about his social skills made us skeptics about his potential as a breeder. The fact that he produced so many offspring was not only a miracle but a boost to attendance and public interest in the zoo. All of his offspring became famous in their own right. Baby gorillas are among the cutest of all zoo animals, and gorillas are right behind baby pandas in generating revenue and donations. Our giant panda exhibit had a branded gift shop (Pandamonium), but the gorillas could have been just as successful with a stand-alone shop. I'm sorry I didn't think about the opportunity when I was chief executive. Our need to be inclusive meant we had to market plush toys for all of our animals on exhibit. My own children are the proud owners of lots of Willie B. memorabilia. When I was general curator at Audubon Zoo, I wrote a script for the zoo train, and we renamed the train the Mombasa Railroad. Most zoos today adopt the names of exotic places to simulate the experience of an African safari. The Willie B. brand is strong and still recognizable in Atlanta. At one time, I believe his reputation in marketing circles was stronger than that of any local human celebrity In fact, celebrities ranging from politicians such as President Jimmy Carter to athletes such as Henry Aaron came to see him. The writer Pat Conroy had a special visit with Willie B. and the black rhino, Boma, on a tour with me on the occasion of the great silverback's birthday. Had we been greedy, we would have hired an agent to peddle his image. His endorsement would likely have helped to market all kinds of products, and the royalties would have made the zoo a lot of money.

FIGURE 10-3. SANTA GORILLA UNMASKED (D. FITZGERALD).

If current Zoo Atlanta leadership is as business savvy as I think they are, they will soon begin to plan the brand future of Willie B. Jr. His façade could generate funding for the zoo for the next twenty years or more. In the meantime, zoos in Atlanta and throughout the nation will continue to offer giraffe feeding and portraits with small educational animals. For many years, Singapore Open Zoo offered a moment of teatime with the female orangutan Ah Meng because she was tractable and friendly, although the inherent danger of such close proximity with a large ape or large cat discourages most responsible zoos from arranging these experiences. In fact, many zoo associations consider this form of contact exploitive and unethical. However, some animal experts, such as Jim Fowler of Omaha's Wild Kingdom, have argued that the knowledge gained from close contact is worth the risk.

The motivation to get close to wildlife is so strong that most zoo directors have at least one photograph of themselves with an animal in their collection. The most photographed celebrity ape is the signing gorilla, Koko, who has attracted visitors from far and wide for the opportunity to meet her up close and personal. Visitors to the Willie B. Conservation Center building sat across a large glass barrier to get an intimate look at Willie B. and his family. Often the baby gorillas would bang on the glass to get the attention of children on the other side. Safe play with gorillas was built into our innovative observation structure in the Ford African Rain Forest.

Although Willie B. is one of the most famous of all silverback gorillas, he is not alone in the power of his image and reputation. Male gorillas in Chicago, Philadelphia, San Diego, London, and Basel, Switzerland, were among the best known in their time. Ringling Brothers' Gargantua generated the most hyperbole, but the circus is not constrained by the demand for honesty. In the circus, a goat with one horn can be presented as a unicorn, but a zoo must acknowledge that the animal is simply a one-horned goat. As educational institutions, zoos have to operate at a different standard. What the circus teaches us is that the potential for marketing charismatic animals is virtually unlimited.

An article about John Daniel, a lowland gorilla brought up as a boy in the English village of Uley, attracted a lot of attention at the time. John Daniel was purchased from a department store by British major Rupert Penny in 1917 for the sum of 34,000 U.S. dollars. He had been captured in Gabon. The major could not provide proper care for the animal, so he sent him to his sister Alyce Cunningham. Because she had no idea how to raise an ape, Ms. Cunningham raised him as if he were her own human child. He played with children in the village and accompanied her on trips to London, but he eventually became too large to control. He spent three happy years in England and is still remembered by people in the village. She reluctantly sold him to a wealthy American businessman who betrayed her confidence by selling him to the circus. John Daniel died soon after he was acquired by Ringling Brothers. His short life among humanity demonstrates the adaptability of gorillas.

Although zoo purists don't approve of excessive hyperbole with iconic zoo animals, it would be foolish not to promote the animals when private, voluntary revenue generated through attendance and in-park spending is necessary to keep zoos in the black. Only heavily subsidized government-operated zoos can afford to resist marketing and branding opportunities. Frankly, I am encouraged by the demand for corporate partnerships due to the high popularity of key species and the zoo itself. It wasn't always so.

Willie's life has been documented in print and electronic media. Mayor Andrew Young and Monica Kaufman narrated a film for local television that followed the mayor on his travels to Africa and featured the story of our hometown gorilla. *The Life and Times of Willie B.* was eventually distributed in dozens of other cities, no doubt influencing the fate of many other gorillas waiting for improvements in their quality of life. With the insight of a successful politician, Mayor Young observed: "He had a personality. Women would throw him kisses and he'd come up to the window and press his lips on it. He interacted with the people."

Chapter 11

A DIRECTOR'S WORST NIGHTMARE

Willie B. began to suffer the symptoms of heart failure in 1999. We conferred with the best cardiologists at Emory University to treat his condition. He was forty years old, but we had high hopes he would live much longer. The solitary male gorilla Massa, at the Philadelphia Zoo, established the record for longevity in captivity by living to the grand old age of fifty-four. At the end of Massa's life, he looked very old. By contrast, Willie B.'s vigor had been well demonstrated by his successful breeding history, and he occupied a very stable family of adult females and assorted offspring. He lived in the largest of our four habitats with a large window, so he was accessible to his adoring human friends. Willie actually liked people and enjoyed coming close to the crowd when snacks were presented to him and he could eat and quietly play with his offspring.

However, we could see that he was slowing down, and we began to contemplate a future without the great silverback. On the day he died, Ground Hog Day 2000, I was recruiting a new general curator. I was in the middle of a pitch to our leading candidate, Dr. Dwight Lawson, when my staff knocked on my door to deliver the bad news. As wonderful as Dwight turned out to be, he was small compensation for the loss of Willie B. Of course, no man or beast could ever replace him. Willie B. died in his sleep during the lunch hour as he occupied a small treatment cage in the gorilla night house. Keepers and veterinarians were at lunch away from the zoo when it happened, but I was grateful that Mike Hoff was in the building observing gorillas that day. He was able to assure me that Willie B. passed away peacefully, a victim of myocardial fibrosis.

Mike was the last person to see Willie B. alive, but he has another distinction. Mike has been continuously observing gorillas at Yerkes and the zoo since 1976. He stopped watching them in 2018, after his retirement from the faculty at Dalton College, a period of forty-two years. No other behavioral scientist has watched gorillas longer. And no one knows the Zoo Atlanta gorillas better than Mike does. Even in our retirement, our collaboration continues, so the reader can expect to see additional publications.

Our veterinarian, Dr. Rita McManamon, had worked diligently to save Willie B., but I was in denial to the bitter end. Emory's cardiologists delivered advice and medication for the great silverback, knowing that he was truly a very important primate. This early participation by Emory faculty and the eventual inclusion of biomedical engineers at Georgia Tech laid the foundation for the award-winning Zoo Atlanta Heart Project, a national program of research that monitors and investigates cardiac history in every gorilla enrolled in the AZA species survival program. This turned out to be another benefit of our broad partnership with universities in our region.

Zoo Atlanta has become one of our nation's best examples of an empirical zoo (Maple and Lindburg, 2008). Cleveland Zoo is a key player in this unique AZA partnership led by my former student Dr. Kristen Lukas. Rita and Kristen worked together on nutritional issues for gorillas when Kristen was a graduate student. I hired Rita in part because she had the skills of a scientist to complement her clinical background. My old friend Hal Markowitz introduced me to Rita, and I immediately began to recruit her for the challenge of building a new zoo in Atlanta. Rita was raised in California as Addie and I were, and we knew it would take a hard sell for her to leave the West Coast and settle in the south. But things were happening in Atlanta that made it the perfect location for zoological enterprise and innovations in zoological medicine. Dr. Rita, as she is known, breathed life into our underachieving, controversial veterinary program, mending fences and uplifting everyone around her. Now retired from the zoo, her new role at the University of Georgia Veterinary College provides services for many of the zoos she routinely assembled for medical collaboration in Atlanta.

The public response to Willie B.'s loss was immediate and powerful. People called and wrote to me to demand a service to celebrate his life. I was uneasy about services for a gorilla, but I was encouraged by a conversation with Mayor Andrew Young. Just hours after Willie B. passed away, I asked the mayor, an ordained minister, if he would have any misgivings about delivering a eulogy for a gorilla. He agreed that it was a unique opportunity and certainly appropriate, committing to participate the Saturday following Willie's death.

More than 8,000 Atlanta citizens attended the service, and many more were turned away due to the massive crowd assembled in Grant Park. Such devotion to local animals is not unusual in the zoo world. The passing of Suri the white tiger at Audubon Zoo in New Orleans lured more than 20,000 fans to the zoo to celebrate her life. Other iconic animals have been mourned at the moment of their passing as the media and local citizens sang their praises. In Bangkok, Thailand, an ape received Buddhist funeral rites after Mike, a popular orangutan at the Sa Kaew Zoo, passed away in 2002. The Atlanta event was a beautiful service highlighted by Reverend Young's emotional prose. He spoke eloquently about the meaning of Willie B.'s life and his service to humanity. A portion of the Mayor's remarks follows with his permission:

> We looked at him in his cage and we knew that he didn't belong there. He was brought here in captivity, but he found a way to appeal to our hearts so that we were moved to find ways to set him free. And in setting him free, perhaps we set ourselves free to help us learn that we can live together in peace with all of the animals that God has created . . . The zoo was the first and still the most successful privatization by Atlanta City government . . . Certainly a group of private citizens with a cause, who love the zoo, can do better with their own funds . . . and with their own dedication to the animals of this earth, than we could ever have done with taxpayers' money . . . We don't know what the animals think of us, but we sure know we love them . . . love can be multiplied and can bear fruits that are not unimagined by any of us at present. But when we do see wonderful things happening between men and women and animals, let's remember this giant, lovable gorilla, who was almost human. Or maybe, we were almost really and truly

God's animals when we related to him. Thank God for
Willie B.

From those kind words, it was clear that Willie B. had made a strong
impression on Mayor Young. The audience was so touched by the event
that they stood in line for an hour just to touch his urn and obtain auto-
graphs for their programs. At the end of the day, I walked to the gorilla exhibits with citizens in tow who wanted to pay their final respects to Willie
B.'s family. A highly cohesive group, they were quietly feeding outside and
seemed oblivious to the impact of his loss. Perhaps they were patiently
waiting for him to join them after a lengthy period of isolation for treatment of his heart disease.

As peaceful as the transition appeared, we know from our own research
findings that the loss of a silverback male can be highly disruptive (Hoff
et al., 1982; Hoff et al., 1998). For example, in the 1982 Hoff et al. study,
an experimental separation of a silverback from his group resulted in an
immediate increase in female aggression. Upon his return, order was restored. The construct of control role was supported in this study and found
to be consistent with primate research on other species (Bernstein and
Sharpe, 1966; de Waal, 1977). In another experimental separation, Hoff et
al. (1994) confined three 27-month-old infants in a cage away from their
mothers and the resident silverback. The infants initially emitted threats
consistent with the symptoms of anaclitic depression in children. Several
days later, they began to cling to each other and exhibited self-holding and
fetal huddling, characteristics of the despair phase of depression (Bowlby,
1968). We'll never know how the gorillas in his family suffered from Willie
B.'s sudden demise, but Willie's loss was real even if his human fans found
it so hard to accept. In life and in death, he made the entire city weep.

I have to disagree with one point the mayor made. The private investment of funding and love was critical to our mission of rebuilding the
zoo, but city/county funding was also essential. The initial construction
effort, which included the Ford African Rain Forest exhibit, was funded by
revenue bonds through the Atlanta-Fulton County Recreation Authority.
Later, the zoo benefited from a $2.5 million grant from the State of

Georgia. This robust grant from the General Assembly was made possible by Lt. Governor Mark Taylor. We reciprocated by agreeing to mentor the Chehaw Park Nature Reserve in South Georgia. We helped them to eventually achieve accreditation in AZA, but they later abandoned their membership to market their site as an "attraction." Hopefully, they will not abandon the high operating standards that they adopted during our mentoring partnership.

Over the years, Mark proved to be a great friend of the zoo who helped me understand how to utilize government services. He envisioned a zoo that was more of a statewide resource. To meet this objective, we created the Zoological Foundation of Georgia with access to state funding. Our relationship with Lt. Governor Taylor led to an invitation from Governor Joe Frank Harris, who arranged for me to join a state delegation seeking trade with China. These contacts eventually culminated in the loan of giant pandas to Zoo Atlanta. We weren't as well known as zoos like San Diego and Bronx, but we had powerful friends in our local, state, and federal governments. Corporate partners such as Delta Airlines, Bell South, United Parcel Service, Coca-Cola, and Ford also strengthened our application. When you are climbing the ladder to greatness, you cannot have enough friends. Working in telecommunications in China, Bell South executives helped me to properly entertain the Chinese delegation that hosted my visit.

When Zell Miller became governor, he included Zoo Atlanta in his statewide plan to upgrade distance learning capabilities in schools throughout the state. We became one of his most reliable producers of content for the public school system. Unfortunately, after Governor Miller left office, there were no programs created to fund the system, and it eventually was replaced by less expensive technologies. I'm proud of the fact that we proved many years ago that kids could learn from expert distant presentations as long as those presentations were exciting.

Chapter 12

TESTIMONIALS AND TRIBUTES TO THE GREATEST APE

After Willie B. passed away, he was difficult to forget. Citizens in Atlanta and throughout the South mourned his loss by publishing letters to the editor in many newspapers and by contacting the zoo director's office just to shout out their affection for this magnificent creature. At the time of his death, he was arguably the most famous gorilla in the world. He was so well known that he became the symbol for professional soccer in Atlanta. The owners of the new Silverbacks franchise selected Willie B. as the mascot for this team and donated money to help the zoo. I was stunned by their generosity and the significance of this decision. Nonhuman primate nicknames are rare in the sports world. I know of only one other example, the Gorillas of Pittsburg State, Kansas.

Due to the volume of correspondence devoted to celebrating his life, I decided to collect as much material as I could from his fans and friends. He was loved by rich and poor, young and old, and even those curmudgeons who really didn't like zoos. What follows is a sample of the material I collected with the help of Gail Eaton. We received dozens of letters, cards, and phone calls of condolences from a wide variety of people: celebrities and media figures, corporate leaders, academics, zoo directors, and citizens from every walk of life. Willie B.'s life touched so many people, and they wanted me to know that they experienced a profound sadness on his passing. The former CEO of Coca-Cola Company, Doug Ivester, grew up in Gainesville, Georgia. He had this to say about Willie B:

I remember Willie B. in the early days. We watched him grow in stature and nobility, displaying an amazing patience with our city. His long patience was rewarded as Atlanta finally provided him a home befitting his status.

Sam Massell, former Atlanta mayor from 1970 to 1974 who became president of the Buckhead Business Coalition, expressed his fond memories of our beloved silverback in the following words excerpted from his letter:

> It's heartwarming when humans address the needs and care of animals, being sensitive to their comforts and emotions . . . I can recall sadly the deplorable state of affairs in our zoo when I was a child. Years later I became president of the Atlanta Humane Society and was able to bring about some reforms to exercise love and respect for all living creatures. Willie B. held a special place in this kingdom and I was proud that our mayor and his namesake, Bill Hartsfield, took his presence seriously.

Actress Stefanie Powers, a conservation advocate and naturalist in her own right, made a film with me (*Search for the Red Ape*) and helped our zoo in countless ways over the years. During her many visits to Atlanta, she was impressed with Willie B. and witnessed his introduction into the wilds of the Ford African Rain Forest at its Grand Opening in 1988.

> The day he was released was the most extraordinary moment of all. To watch him sitting inside his doorway, insecure about the outside world—looking back at his reactions as he touched his finger to the ground and then to his nose to smell this environment so new to him and yet it must have triggered some long-forgotten nostalgia from his infancy . . . His story and his personality is such an inspiration to us all I feel grateful to share with all his other admirers the wonder and joy of observing this extraordinary

individual. If there is a gorilla heaven, I hope Willie B. has found a great big puffy cloud to rest on.

I was moved by the comments of Robert Mobley, a longtime friend of the zoo whose affection for Willie B is evident. In a letter to me, he wrote the following:

> My heart was wounded by the news of Willie B.'s death. In my home this morning, I stood in front of Carole Hutchinson's etching of Kinyani and Willie B. that was created from our photographs of Willie B. As I recall, the duplicate etching that Sherril and I donated for the 1991 Beastly Feast was acquired by Ford Motor Company. I reflected upon those early Beastly Feasts, the opening of the Ford African Rain Forest and the freeing of Willie B. I wept.

I was ten years old when I first heard his name. Soon going to Grant Park meant running to the new monkey house to see Willie B. . . . His searching eyes, playful spirit and sometimes hand touch, albeit behind the glass, pulled at every human's soul. No one said it, but we all wondered if Willie B. was much different from us.

Board member and benefactor Kathleen Day, whose family traveled with me in Africa, leading to a significant gift that helped us design the Ford gorilla exhibit and build the Masai Mara African Savannah exhibit, loved Willie B. After his passing, she wrote:

> I'll never forget the time you took some of your Tech students over to observe him. I was enthralled by your ability to communicate with him. You both had these devilish glimmers in your eyes as you teased each other. You knew his language and he seemed to welcome this interaction with you, a joyful break from a boring existence. Even then, you treated him with the respect he deserved.

Willie did seem to have mixed feelings about me; I was at once a competitor (huge and hairy as my graduate student mentor used to say) and a friend who introduced significant change into his life.

Former zoo director Steve Dobbs had great affection for Willie B. despite his narrow training in herpetology. On my first day at the zoo in 1975, Steve proudly introduced me to him as if Willie B. was a member of his family. In a letter after Willie passed away, he expressed his early impressions of Willie B.

> In those days Willie was afraid of reptiles. Whenever he
> was reluctant to go into his night-time shift cage, keepers
> from the mammal department would borrow one of our
> turtles or a snake to use in scaring Willie into his bedroom.
> Later, as zoo director . . . Willie received a tv set from a
> fan. Visitors would crowd around the tv to see what show
> he was watching, when in reality he was watching them.
> Willie was a people watcher! I had often dreamed of modi-
> fying Willie's quarters . . . sadly, for me this was not to be.
> After twenty years of service, I retired. Happily, Willie was
> a priority with Zoo Atlanta's new director. Terry invited me
> to Willie B.'s coming out party. I watched as Willie first set
> foot in the great outdoors. It was a wonderful experience to
> see Willie with the earth beneath his feet and the sky above
> his head. I recall feeling peace of mind, joy in my heart and
> a tear in my eye.

One of the most dedicated volunteers for the Atlanta Zoological Society, Lucy Chiles, visited him often in her role as a docent. Lucy and her close friend, Pat McCurdy, knew a lot about him and taught others about his life and their hopes for his future. She told me the story of how she played with him from the perimeter of his cage.

> I often cried for Willie the many years we ran together in
> the old primate building where he lived caged for 27 years.

I ran outside of his cage as he ran inside. He always recognized me as I entered the building and usually would come to greet me in anticipation of our running game, thumping his chest in disapproval of my husband if he were with me .
. . The last time I saw Willie, he was at the top of the hill of his habitat and he immediately came down in front of the viewing window to greet me, and I shed both happy and sad tears. We no longer ran together, for he had his own family to romp with.

Reggie Williams served as the chief executive of the Atlanta-Fulton County Recreation Authority when we were in the process of privatizing the zoo. Reggie was a great fan of Willie B. and an important government leader who advanced our cause within local government. Reggie sent me the following message in a letter shortly after the great silverback passed. He expressed an interesting perspective on the meaning of freedom.

I have many fond memories of Willie B. I will never forget the first day he stepped into the rain forest. Some people would surely say I'm stretching things, but I felt the way when Willie B. was freed that I felt when Mandela was freed. Life without freedom is nothing.

We were also touched by the thoughtful statement of Stan Mullins:

Hearing the news of Willie B.'s passing brought tears of sadness and pride to my eyes. Sadness at the loss of a friend, and pride in knowing that this dear friend embodied so much for all of nature, and that he touched countless people. Upon first meeting him and having the pleasure of painting him, while artist in residence there at the zoo, he became a grandfather of all the other gorillas I would meet in Rwanda during my travels to the Virunga Gorilla Preserve . . . While Willie B. is gone, his legacy lives on.

His courage, character, and destiny have helped to promote
a new kind of conservation and reverence for life.

Dan Ashe is the chief executive of the Association of Zoos and
Aquariums and formerly the director of the U.S. Fish and Wildlife Service
in the Department of Interior. He grew up in Atlanta and has fond memories of family visits to see Willie B. at the zoo. Willie's plight was so inspiring that Dan gives him much of the credit for his own conservation
achievements. He wrote the following testimonial:

> Many animals suffered during my adolescent awakening
> to nature and sense of wonder for wild life and wild places,
> including snakes, lizards, crayfish, turtles, birds, and scores
> of insects. But one played an outsize role, the lowland go-
> rilla named Willie B . . . He endured an unimaginable soli-
> tary captivity until Grant Park Zoo was transformed into
> Zoo Atlanta, providing him with a modern habitat where
> he lived as a gorilla with other gorillas. So, in requiem, I
> offer apology to Willie B. for his suffering, gratitude for
> the inspiration he provided for my career in wildlife con-
> servation, and a share in credit for accomplishments, like
> establishing and protecting some of the world's most amaz-
> ing and enduring conservation areas, battling trafficking
> in wild animals, and ending the trade in elephant ivory.
> Thank you, Willie B.

My longtime friend, colleague, and mentor, Professor Donald G.
Lindburg, formerly director of conservation and science at the Zoological
Society of San Diego, offered some creative thoughts about Willie B., the
animal who inspired many world zoos to upgrade their facilities. In Don's
words:

> The story of Willie B. captivated us all and at no time did
> the drama reach a greater climax than when he had stepped

out into the out-of-doors and eventually to renewed contact with his own kind, after a lifetime of isolated living . . . . My own institution was engaged in planning for Gorilla Tropics, a modern, state-of-the-art exhibit and breeding center <we invited> Dr. Terry Maple to San Diego for consultation . . . and an evening of celebrating the wonder of gorillas. My assignment was to introduce him . . . so I pulled out a little poem I had read a few days before, and with modification used it to introduce Terry (with apologies to its author Ralph Lewin):

> The Chinese Hamster copulates
> At fifty times the rate of us apes.
> This is to him a source of pride.
> It keeps his hamstress satisfied.
> And soon (if books can be believed.
> Ten little hamlets are conceived.
> But ten new babies in a house
> Are overmuch for ape or mouse.
> Compared with him, I'd be content—
> In both respects—with ten percent.

Looking back on the life that was Willie B., we all take pleasure in noting that, more than once, he gave us his "ten percent." Given Professor Lindburg's vast experience in field and zoo primatology, his remarks about Willie B. demonstrated how much the great silverback had inspired him. Many colleagues at the San Diego Zoo have favorably compared Willie B. to their iconic silverback, Albert. When I was a student enrolled in calculus at San Diego Mesa College in the summer of 1966, I frequently played hooky to visit Albert at the zoo in Balboa Park. He was a truly noble and awesome specimen. My parents knew I admired this animal, and they presented me one Christmas with a framed photo of one of Albert's iconic poses. You cannot look at this image without concluding he was a thinker.

He was so popular in San Diego that the zoo named its signature restaurant Albert's.

It was an honor to speak on behalf of San Diego Zoo leaders who sought my endorsement of their new plan for a gorilla exhibit. I stood outside our exhibit with Willie B. in the background and proudly looked into the camera to proclaim, "San Diego used to be the world's leader in gorilla exhibitory, but the torch has been passed. If the citizens of San Diego respond to this message, a state-of-the-art gorilla facility will be built and San Diego will once again be recognized for its leadership in the management and exhibition of great apes." I'm happy to say that the zoo was successful in raising $1 million with this video presentation.

When I returned to my home town to accept an award for my role in the production, it was a proud moment indeed. It was also my pleasure to supervise the post-occupancy evaluation of their new exhibit, a study conducted for her dissertation by Jackie Ogden (Ogden et al., 1993a, 1993b; Ogden et al., 1994). Jackie and I both grew up in San Diego County, and we both became leaders in the profession. Jackie worked at the San Diego Zoo before she was recruited to the new Disney's Animal Kingdom. She was so successful in her career at San Diego, Disney, and AZA that she was awarded the prestigious Marlin Perkins Award in 2018. Jackie and I can boast that we are zoo alumni educated through the great outreach of the world-famous San Diego Zoo. Atlanta now has an educational asset comparable to the one that I enjoyed as a kid. As the investigator who evaluated Willie B.'s liberation (Ogden et al., 1990), she had this to say about the experience:

> The opportunity to meet Willie B. and to watch him through his incredible life transitions was indeed a privilege . . . He taught us all many lessons, the greatest probably of the value of resilience. He was an amazing ape--clearly intelligent, and almost astoundingly well-adjusted given the challenge of his first years. I give his caregivers, especially Charles Horton, credit for this. They worked with him in a way that reinforced his natural behaviors and encouraged

him to be a gorilla. And he definitely was. My late husband, Hall Elliott, grew up in Atlanta, and he wrote a poem about the transformation that Terry and his team wrought, including a reference to Willie B. In Hall's own words:

"I went to the zoo at the age of five; the animals seemed to be barely alive; The dead-eyed tiger paced behind the bars; The scruffy lion showed his "handling" scars; I went today to the same location; Seemed to be an African vacation; Habitats seemed to leave animals free; Kinyani brings new life to Willie B."

My former student, Mike Hoff, a retired professor at Dalton State College and a highly experienced observer of zoo gorillas, had his own lifetime perspective on Willie B. He submitted a thoughtful essay entitled "Willie B: Past and Present," which contained many fascinating details, including the last quiet moments of Willie B.'s life. Mike confirmed that he died peacefully at 2:00 p.m., February 2, 2000. He was the only human witness in the final moments of the great silverback's life.

The degree of success of Willie's socialization became apparent as he copulated with Kinyani on the first day of their release together outdoors. Willie spent several years with Katoomba and Kinyani. His social skills were honed by the ongoing interactions with the females. He looked and acted like a typical silverback male gorilla. Yet, there were no offspring. Choomba, the mother of Machi, was introduced to Willie in October, 1992 and Shamba was introduced and Katoomba removed in March 1993. Choomba is a large female who doesn't hesitate to show dominance behaviors. Yet, she was a proven breeder. This change worked. Choomba gave birth to the female, Kudzoo, on February 8, 1994, 16 months after Choomba's introduction to Willie B.

We owe a debt of gratitude to Mike, who spent more hours with Willie B. and the other Zoo Atlanta gorillas than anyone other than our zookeepers. His careful notes over four decades supplemented the daily observations of his caregivers and helped the team to make good decisions about his transitions and opportunities. An observer of Mike's experience is a tremendous asset for any zoo breeding colony. Mike's high productivity was another benefit of his participation and leadership. He wrote many research papers for publication in refereed journals, adding to the credibility of our scientific program.

To qualify as an empirical zoo, professionals like Dr. Hoff are absolutely necessary. In an essay published in APS *Observer* (Hoff, 2004), Mike summarized the challenge of his research at Zoo Atlanta:

> My primary research challenge relates to time. I need large blocks of time to be able to travel the 90 miles to Zoo Atlanta one or two days per week, and I need time to analyze data and write papers. There have been two primary keys to my being able to do this: collaboration and technology . . . By combining data and sharing data analysis and writing responsibilities, we are able to develop a better understanding of gorillas in a captive environment and regularly publish our results.

Another scientist with an appreciation of Willie B. is Dr. Tara Stoinski, chief scientific officer and CEO of the Dian Fossey Gorilla Fund. In addition to her work in Africa, Tara has studied zoo gorillas for two decades. Given her administrative duties, her research productivity is remarkable. She is the ultimate collaborator who invited many distinguished scientists and distant institutions to work with our team in Atlanta. She and her best friend Dr. Kristen Lukas have helped each other to continue their involvement with gorilla conservation and science. As the current chair of the SSP Gorilla Committee, Kristen has been particularly effective in organizing colleagues to investigate heart disease and nutrition in zoo gorillas. As two of the most accomplished students of gorilla behavior, Kristen and

Tara both trace their academic roots to Atlanta with doctoral degrees from Georgia Tech, and they have many memories of Willie B. and the Yerkes gorillas. In a personal note, Tara offered the following comments about our common friend, Willie B.

> Willie B.'s life inspired people from around the world to care about gorillas. The stories of his personality, his likes and dislikes, his success in starting a family, created a deep empathy for both him as an individual and his species. He is an example of how animals living in zoos can act as ambassadors for their wild counterparts creating connections to individual animals that hopefully will motivate people to help conserve them in the wild.

Kristen's feelings about Willie B. were expressed in a recent letter she wrote to me:

> . . . it is difficult to capture the extent to which Willie B. affected my career. First and foremost, your efforts to improve his life at Zoo Atlanta spurred studies of gorilla behavior and habitat design that completely inspired and enabled my research interest . . . I'll never forget the sound of the love rumble he would give me—made me feel so special . . . I really feel so privileged to have known him and to have had the chance to learn from him during my time at Zoo Atlanta.

Charles Horton enjoyed a special relationship with Willie B. No one spent more quality time with Willie than Charles. All the time they spent together Charles talked to him. Charles witnessed all the high points of Willie's progression to silverback status. A key player in Willie's transformation, Charles provided the following thoughtful observations on their unique relationship:

In all my years of working at the zoo my best memories are of the time I spent working in the care of Willie B. . . . I was privileged to have one on one time with him. Getting to be in proximity to him to play games of chase and tug of war and hand feed his dinner in the evening were special experiences . . . Willie became the flagship of the reformation of the zoo. First a successful move to a new building, setting foot outside on the grass, his socialization and mating with female gorillas, and the siring of five beautiful gorilla babies were not only great milestones for Zoo Atlanta but for me personally. I was so proud of him.

Finally, our collection of testimonial statements would not be complete without the words of our chief designer, landscape architect Jon Charles Coe. On March 22, 1996, Jon expressed his reflections about Willie B. on the day he was liberated:

He was locked up like a sideshow freak or felon, but Willie B. never acted like a felon. He acted like an ambassador, without portfolio, without rights, without freedom; but ambassador all the same . . . We are spellbound by the new Willie B., as if the power of the trees, and grass, and boulders had magnified his already substantial charisma. As if the chains of human domination have fallen, revealing Willie in his full majesty. Yet, Willie hasn't changed. We have. For the first time we see him as he really is.

In addition to the accolades and sympathy generated by the passing of Willie B., friends of the zoo also generously donated funding to complete the life-size sculpture of dear Willie B. Renee and Dennis Hopf were particularly committed to funding this program, and their support on a wide variety of issues is much appreciated. Over the years, our corporate and foundation community gave generously to upgrade the zoo. During this active development period, we were ably led by Clare Richardson and loyal board members who were constantly on the move pursuing gifts. By the time I met the benefactors, they were already sold on the zoo as an urgent cause. I saw my role as the closer when, like a lion in the final stages of a hunt, I symbolically "bit the neck and closed the deal." We had so many donors over the years—corporations, foundations, and individuals—I could never thank them enough. Of course, as I've said before, the real closer was Willie B. You could not say no to Willie B.

When I visit the zoo, I always treasure the moment when I can sit next to his image and remember the quality time we spent together during his active life at the zoo. Often, I step back from the visitors gathered at the site, just to remember how much he still means to his entire city of fans and friends. I miss him terribly. At such times, he brings out the silverback in all of us.

Epilogue

PERSONAL REFLECTIONS ON
THE LIFE OF WILLIE B.

Willie B. lived through years of adversity, but he was indeed a very resilient creature. Although he was formidable in his appearance, I liked him immediately. Silverbacks, even singletons, are fascinating. They attract attention from other gorillas and from the people who pay good money to see them. By the end of Willie's life, with five offspring, he was a full-fledged silverback. In my profession, I too had reached silverback status, with three offspring and twenty-seven graduate students under my belt. Looking back to our introduction in 1975, it has been a remarkable journey for a single gorilla, a young professor, and an underachieving zoo.

Willie B. educated millions of young people who learned about him on school trips to the zoo. He was so impressive that the memory of this great ape remains long into our adulthood. His story is a metaphor for the zoo itself, and he played a major role in elevating our stature as a credible zoological park. It was an improbable story of recovery and revitalization, and a model for other zoos seeking to improve the quality of life for their entire population of animals. During his forty-one years on this earth, he taught us volumes about how to elevate our respect for animals and how to deal with adversity with dignity. In his quiet way, he was certainly a mentor to me. I am comforted by the fact that what we learned from Willie B. and others like him will ensure that no gorilla will ever have to suffer like he did. Modern zoos would never capture or kill a wild gorilla, and they would violate our code of ethics if they failed to meet the current high standards of animal welfare enacted by AZA and other accrediting bodies.

Gorillas are social beings, and they should never be isolated from their own kind. I'm proud of Zoo Atlanta's role in elevating these standards and the many animals we liberated in the process.

At the time of his death, he was the oldest gorilla in North America who had sired offspring. The stimulation of his family surely added years to his life. The story of his rehabilitation and resocialization may be the greatest zoo story ever told. Other zoo directors did not envy me when I took the reins of a dilapidated zoo, but after eighteen years of reform, they all would have gladly traded places with me to experience the joy of Zoo Atlanta's revitalization. Indeed, the visibility of the Ford African Rain Forest exhibit influenced other zoos to follow suit. This has created demand for breeding units. If the demand is fulfilled, it could diminish the complexity of better exhibits designed for larger numbers of gorillas. I feel strongly that we have to protect the integrity of the population approach we pioneered in Atlanta. When the zoo elected to add more male groups, it worried me, but it turned out to be a temporary shift in emphasis. The upside of this decision was the leadership provided by Zoo Atlanta's growing expertise in the management of all male groups.

The Willie B. story is Atlanta's story. To this end, Mike Hoff and I are continuing our educational collaboration with an op-ed we have written for Father's Day 2021. Dedicated to Willie B., a wonderful father that we followed throughout his adult life, this is a story that needs to be remembered. Strong fathers (silverbacks all) are essential elements in the normal developmental process of young apes. It is true of humans as well. Absent fathers, young men often go astray. Mike and I had strong fathers that we revered, and we hope we have been the role models that our daughters needed. The text of this op-ed is available as an appendix to this book. I have also republished an essay I wrote shortly after Willie B.'s death ("The Power of One"). His story moved the Atlanta community, but it also resonated within the halls of academe and among zoo professionals globally.

HOW THE ZOO WAS WON

Atlanta's public/private partnership empowered the new nonprofit board to adopt entrepreneurial business practices. Zoo Atlanta and others that privatized later won their freedom from stifling government bureaucracies. Lincoln Park Zoo, in Chicago, negotiated a continuing subsidy from the city capped at $7 million of operating support. Once the private contributions came in, the zoo's coffers swelled and new projects bloomed.

As entrepreneurial entities with greater access to private funding, zoos raised their standards to achieve unqualified excellence. Elegant visions of naturalistic nature parks were rendered by some of the nation's finest architecture firms. North American zoos, once ignored by the intelligentsia, became almost overnight the envy of the world. The best zoos, like San Diego, have become cultural icons. Some designers branded their works as a return to Eden, doing all they could to blend botanicals with wildlife in an accurate simulation of the natural world. Today, every aspirational zoo has become a certified zoological and botanical garden. Such places celebrate biodiversity in unique ways.

Art is another way to celebrate the wonder of wildlife. We commissioned many sculptures during my time at the zoo, and we hired artists to render oil paintings of our founders and friends. The zoo board authorized paintings of Robert M. Holder, Carolyn Hatcher, Robert Strickland, Marvin Arrington, Andrew Young, and Dr. Mort Silberman. These leaders are deserving of this recognition, but I have vivid memories of all of them as they worked together to reimagine our city zoo.

FIGURE E-1. MY FATHER WAS PLAYFUL AND THE FOCUS OF OUR FAMILY LIFE.

Our construction plan was highly professional thanks to board member Mack Taylor and his right-hand men, Harvey Cheatham and Jimmy Wren. As first-rate developers, they managed the money and the labor as if the zoo were one of their favorite construction projects. At an early board meeting, I was telling a story about an emerald tree boa that I wanted to purchase for the zoo. Mack asked me how much it would cost, and he promptly wrote a check so I could buy it. He loved telling that story himself.

Every zoo provides access for school-age kids to submit their artistic interpretations of our animals. We rotated kids' drawings in our administrative building to keep staff aware that the zoo was dedicated to public education. We kept kids in the loop on our reforms by creating classes on zoo design and construction. We crafted hard hats for the children to wear and took them to see exhibits as they unfolded in the park. My daughter Emily and the daughter of a neighbor attended the same elementary school. At a show and tell session, Emily bragged that her father ran the zoo. Her friend's father was one of the zoo engineers, and she one-upped Emily with the retort, "Well, my father built the zoo!"

I always intended to organize walking tours of the zoo's art collection, but I wasn't the first administrator who introduced art at the zoo. City fathers selected Georgia Tech sculptor Julian Harris (1906–1987) to sculpt several terra cotta murals of big cats. They were beautifully executed and visible in the old feline house for many years. After renovation, we didn't have a proper venue for them, so we put them in storage. I hope future leaders will find a location where they can be displayed once again. If I still had an office in the zoo, I would put one of them on the wall behind my desk.

I met Harris when he toured the zoo shortly after I was named director. At the time, we were knocking down the wall behind the bear exhibits. He casually remarked that he had designed these walls to disappear into the skyline. This was news to me, so I apologized, but he was not upset about the changes. The same design was retained at the back of our gorilla exhibit, so his design solution has survived for those who know to look for it. The zoo's sculpture collection includes running cheetahs, reclining lions, a lowland gorilla pair with baby, a baby elephant, an adult-size Komodo dragon, and of course Willie B., all of them cast in bronze. To add to these pieces, our Conservation Action Resources Center won an Urban Design Award for design excellence. This curvilinear structure features a living roof of resilient plants. Art, botanicals, theatre, and wildlife all thrive in a naturalistic zoo that is programmed as an authentic simulation of the natural world.

With the publication of this book on the life of Willie B., Atlanta citizens have bragging rights for the part they played in his renewal. I've tried to thank many people to deflect the credit broadly throughout our community, but I confess I probably missed some important leaders. At seventy-five, my memory isn't what it used to be, but everyone who participated should know that I appreciated each and every step we took together. Several of my close colleagues read drafts of the manuscript, but needless to say, any mistakes or omissions are entirely mine.

On the long road to our reform and recovery, I became an expert on crisis management and a consultant to troubled institutions. I frankly found it easier to offer advice than it was to deal with my own problems, but my peers in the zoo profession were eager to follow our lead. There were days at the zoo when the job was so overwhelming, I didn't want to go to work. Fortunately, when the stress was unbearable, I could visit my office at Georgia Tech. The encouragement of my faculty colleagues was enough to boost my morale and strengthen my resolve. It is too bad that every zoo director cannot have a tenured faculty position to provide job security. Given our unique surroundings, I discovered fairly quickly that the best therapy for office stress was to get out of the office and into the zoo itself. Communing with the animals, especially Willie B., was strong tonic for recovery and renewal, and a major advantage of working in a zoo.

The record of achievement of my staff and students made them all candidates for jobs in bigger, wealthier zoological parks, and I lost many of them to Disney's Animal Kingdom when it opened. These were always happy transitions as I was proud of their achievements and confident that I would be able to recruit capable replacements. But some transitions were painful, and the case of my deputy director, Jeff Swanagan, was a tragic example. After successful assignments at the Florida Aquarium and the new Georgia Aquarium, Jeff returned to his roots as CEO of the Columbus Zoo, no longer second fiddle to Jack Hanna. Sadly, we lost him to a heart attack in the prime of his life. The entire profession misses him. He was a powerhouse educator and a strong leader. On my staff, he mentored everyone he encountered day by day. Had I left the zoo earlier, I feel confident that he would have been the leading candidate to replace me. Jeff hated to leave his family and friends in Atlanta, but he was in demand in Ohio and died in the position he had dreamed about when he started his career at Columbus Zoo.

I can say unequivocally that every one of my staff was proud to work at Zoo Atlanta. They drew inspiration from Willie B. and our collective role in renovation and reform. We held meetings and often congregated socially in the splendid Willie B. Conservation Center adjacent to his family habitat. There we could discuss issues and opportunities while observing the gorillas foraging in their lush surroundings. I once arranged a luncheon in the center with the esteemed biologist E. O. Wilson and our most loyal benefactor, Lessie Smithgall. It was one of the best days of my career.

I had the pleasure of mentoring many bright students who carried out research at the zoo and at Yerkes over the years. My legacy includes many prominent women who are now leaders in the zoo profession and academia. The collaboration of Georgia Tech's School of Psychology and the emerging Zoo Atlanta together with the partnership with Yerkes National Primate Research Center created a unique and dynamic model for reform and innovation.

As scholars and leaders, the women supported by the Elizabeth Smithgall Watts endowment at Tech and the Charles Bailey Fund at Zoo Atlanta made it possible to recruit, retain, and graduate the best and the brightest young people to enter the field. This was a dream I shared with Dr. Watts. Her parents, Charles and Lessie Smithgall of Gainesville, Georgia, provided the financial support to implement the program in Atlanta where baby Bay (as she was known) was first introduced to monkeys at the city zoo by her grandfather, city alderman Charles Bailey. This precious relationship is described in Mrs. Smithgall's delightful autobiography published in

2008. It is especially gratifying to work with a benefactor who is so aware of the issues we must confront in conservation. As this book goes to press, Mrs. Smithgall is about to celebrate her 110th birthday. She is the oldest living member of Phi Beta Kappa. When I talk to her, we spend our time reminiscing about our travel together in Africa. The world is a better place because she chose to use her resources for the betterment of the planet.

My personal experience in the revitalization of Zoo Atlanta leads me to offer this advice: For any institution in crisis, someone has to have the courage to step up, form a cohesive team, and lead. As Ted Turner used to say, "Lead, follow, or get out of the way." Strong leadership is necessary in the early stages of recovery and reform. Even an inexperienced leader can advance the goals of an institution in transition. He or she just has to offer bold solutions and make sure they become part of a new culture of excellence. Teamwork is important, but leadership is essential.

The loss of Willie B. in the year 2000 was a painful blow to my morale. On the heels of the passing of my dear parents, I had reached the end of the line as the leader of Zoo Atlanta. My retirement may have been perceived as sudden, but I had been planning my departure so that it would be as joyful as an Irish wake. Our board of directors greeted this news with compassion and understanding. I gave everything I had in service to the cause. The affection I have for Zoo Atlanta, as its founding president/CEO, has been returned by an entire community of grateful citizens. Atlanta is a great city, and it deserves a great zoo. Great zoos are obligated to do great things. I will expect Zoo Atlanta to continue in its role as a thought leader among the world's elite zoological parks for many years to come. There is much more work to do, as the zoo agenda is broad and deep. In the spirit of Willie B.'s metamorphosis, the future of Zoo Atlanta is alive with opportunity.

semi-mega-sans

FIGURE E-2. CARICATURE OF THE AUTHOR WITH WILLIE B. (GARY H. LEE).

REFERENCES

Abello, M. T., Blasco, and Colell, M. 2011. Could sexually experienced gorillas help hand-reared gorillas to breed successfully? *International Zoo Yearbook* 45, 237-249.

Akeley, C. 1923. *In Brightest Africa*. New York, Doubleday.

Amen, T. 2017. Why you should eat like a wild gorilla. *Huffington Post*.

Anderson, U. S., Stoinski, T. S., Bloomsmith, M. A., and Maple, T. L. 2007. Relative numerousness judgment and summation in young, middle-aged, and older orangutans. *Journal of Comparative Psychology* 121, 1, 1-11.

Anderson, U. S., Stoinski, T. S., Bloomsmith, M. A., Marr, M. J., Smith, A. D., and Maple, T. L. 2005, Relative numerousness judgment and summation in young and old western lowland gorillas. *Journal of Comparative Psychology* 119, 3, 285-295.

Applegate, K. 2012. *The One and Only Ivan*. New York, Harper.

Baker, K. C. 2000. Advanced age influences chimpanzee behavior in small social groups. *Zoo Biology* 19, 2, 111-119.

Beck, B. B., and Power, M. L. 1988. Correlates of sexual and maternal competence in captive gorillas. *Zoo Biology* 7, 339-350.

Bensky, M.K., Gosling, S.D. and Sinn, D.L. 2013. The world from a dog's point of view: a review and synthesis of dog cognition research. *Advances in the Study of Behavior* 45, 209-406.

Bernstein, I.S. and Sharpe, L.G. 1966. Social roles in a rhesus monkey group. *Behaviour* 26, 91-104.

Bowlby, J. 1969. *Attachment and Loss. Vol. 1, Attachment.* New York, Basic Books.

Brown, S. G., Dunlap, W., and Maple, T. L. 1982. Notes on the water-contact behavior of captive lowland gorillas. *Zoo Biology* 1, 3, 243-249.

Burbridge, B. 1928. *Gorilla.* New York, Century.

Burks, K. D., Bloomsmith, M. A., Forthman, D. L., and Maple, T. L. 2001. Managing the socialization of an adult male gorilla (*Gorilla gorilla gorilla*) with a history of social deprivation. *Zoo Biology* 20, 347-358.

Cannataro, G. 2021. SAFE: Taking action. *Connect*, March issue. Bethesda, MD, Association of Zoos and Aquariums, 34-41.

Carpenter, C. R. 1937. An observational study of two captive mountain gorillas (*Gorilla gorilla berengei*). *Human Biology* 9, 175-196.

Chamove, A. S., Eysenck, H. J., and Harlow, H. F. 1972. Personality in monkeys: Factor analyses of rhesus social behaviour. *Quarterly Journal of Experimental Psychology* 24, 496-504.

Choquette, P., Maple, T.L. and Wilson, M. Under editorial review.

Clarke, A. S., Juno, C. R., and Maple, T. L. 1982. Behavioral effects of a change in the physical environment: A pilot study of captive chimpanzees. *Zoo Biology*, 1, 4, 371-380.

Coe, J.C. 1985. Design and Perception: making the zoo experience real. *Zoo Biology* 4,2, 197-208.

Coe, J.C. and Maple, T.L. 1987. In search of Eden: a brief history of great ape exhibits. Wheeling, WVA, *AZA Annual Proceedings*.

Collins, M. E. 2021. Land and sea. *Connect.* Bethesda, MD, Association for Zoos and Aquariums, 28-33.

Costa, R., Mayashi, M., Huffman, M. A., Tikusoka, G. K., and Tomanaga, M. 2019. Water games by mountain gorillas: implications for behavioral development and flexibility—A case report. *Primates* 60, 493-498.

Cousins, D. 1978. The reaction of apes to water. *International Zoo News* 25/7, 8-13.

Davenport, R.K. 1967. The orang-utan in Sabah. *Folia Primatologica* 5, 247-263.

Desiderio, F. 2000. Raising the bars: the transformation of Atlanta's zoo, 1989-2000. *Alanta History: A Journal of Georgia and the South 43, 4, 7-43.*

De Waal, F.B.M. and Lanting, F. 1997. *Bonobo: The Forgotten Ape.* Berkeley, University of California Press.

Du Chaillu, P. 1862. *Explorations and Adventures in Equatorial Africa.* New York, Harper.

Du Chaillu, P. 1899. *Stories of the Gorilla Country.* New York, Harper.

Dybas, C. L. 2007. Out of Africa: A tale of gorillas, heart disease and a swamp plant. *Bioscience* 57, 5, 392-397.

Echardt, W., Steklis, H.D., and Steklis, G. 2014. Personality dimensions and their behavioral correlates in wild Virunga mountain gorillas. *Journal of Comparative Psychology* 16.

Edler, M. K., Sherwood, C. C., Meindl, R. S., Hopkins, W. D., Ely, J. J.,

Ellenberger, H. F. 1960. Zoological garden and mental hospital. *Canadian Psychiatric Association Journal* 5, 3, 136-149.

Ely, J. J., Zavaskis, T., and Lamney, M. L. 2013. Hypertension increases with aging and obesity in chimpanzees (*Pan troglodytes*). *Zoo Biology* 32, 79-87.

Enciso, A. E., Calcagno, J. M., and Gold, K. C. (1999). Social interactions between captive adult male and infant lowland gorillas: Implications regarding kin selection and zoo management. *Zoo Biology* 18, 53-62.

Erwin, J. M., Mufson, E. J., Hof, P. R., and Raghanti, M. A. 2017. Aged chimpanzees exhibit pathological hallmarks of Alzheimer's disease. *Neurobiology of Aging* 7, 6.

Etiendem, D. N., and Tagg, N. 2013. Feeding ecology of Cross River gorillas at Mawambi Hills: The influence of resource seasonality. *International Journal of Primatology* 34, 1261-1280.

Faludi, S. 1991. Backlash: The Undeclared War against American Women.

Finlay, T. W., James, L. R., and Maple, T. L. 1988. Zoo environments influence people's perceptions of animals. *Environment and Behavior* 20, 4, 508-528.

Fossey, D. 1972

Fossey, D. 1983. *Gorillas in the Mist*. New York, Houghton Mifflin.

Fossey, D., and Harcourt, A. H. 1977. Feeding ecology of free-ranging mountain gorillas (*Gorilla gorilla beringei*). In Clutton-Brock, T. H. (Ed.), *Primate Ecology*, 415-447.

Fowler, J. 2019. *A Forest in the Clouds*. New York, Pegasus Books.

Freeman, H. and Gosling, S.L. 2010. Personality in nonhuman primates: a review and evaluation of past research. *American Journal of Primatology* 71, 1-19.

Gallup, G.G. 1970. Chimpanzees: self-recognition. *Science* 167, 86-87.

Gallup, G.G. 1982. Self-awareness and the emergence of mind in primates. *American Journal of Primatology* 2, 3, 237-248.

Gazes, R. P., Diamond, R. F. L., Hope, J. M., Caillaud, D., Stoinski, T. S., and Hampton, R. R. 2017. Spatial representation of magnitude in gorillas and orangutans. *Cognition* 168, 312-319.

Gold, K.C. and Maple, T.L. 1994, Personality assessment in the gorilla and its utility as a management tool. *Zoo Biology* 13, 5, 509-522.

Gold, K. C., and Watson, L. M. 2018. In memoriam: Koko, a remarkable gorilla. *American Journal of Primatology* 80, 12.

Gosling, S.D. 1998. Personality dimensions in spotted hyenas. *Journal of Comparative Psychology* 112, 107-118.

Hamilton, G. V. 1914. A study of sexual tendencies in monkeys and apes. *Animal Behavior* 4, 295-318.

Harcourt, A. H. 1987. Behaviour of wild gorillas and their management in captivity. *International Zoo Yearbook* 26, 248-255.

Harcourt, A. H., and Curry-Lindahl, K. 1979. Conservation of the mountain gorilla and its habitat in Rwanda. *Environmental Conservation* 6, 143-147.

Harcourt, A. H., and Stewart, K. J. 1978. Coprophagy in wild mountain gorillas. *East African Wildlife Journal* 16, 223-225.

Harlow, H. F. 1971. *Learning to Love*. Chicago, Aldine.

Hayes, H. 1977. *The Last Place on Earth*. New York, Stein and Day.

Hediger, H. 1965. *Man and Animal in the Zoo*. London, Routledge and Kegan Paul.

Hendrick, B. 2001. Even in death, Willie B. exerts a potent pull. *Atlanta Journal-Constitution*, April 20.

Hepper, P. G., and Wells, D. L. 2010. Individually identifiable body odors are produced by the gorilla and discriminated by humans. *Chemical Senses* 35, 263-268.

Hodos, W., and Campbell, C. B. G. 1969. Scala Naturae: Why there is no theory in comparative psychology. *Psychological Review* 76, 4, 337-350.

Hoff, M. P. 2004. No monkey business. APS *Observer* 17, 6.

Hoff, M. P., Bloomsmith, M. A., and Zucker, E. L. (Eds.). 2014. *Celebrating the Career of Terry L. Maple; A Festschrift*. Tequesta, FL, Red Leaf Press, 239-252.

Hoff, M. P., Nadler, R. D., Hoff, K. T., and Maple, T. L. 1994. Separation and depression in infant gorillas. *Developmental Psychobiology* 27, 7, 439-452.

Hoff, M. P., Nadler, R. D., and Maple, T. L. 1981a. The development of infant independence in a captive group of lowland gorillas. *Developmental Psychobiology* 14, 251-265.

Hoff, M. P., Nadler, R. D., and Maple, T. L. 1981b. The development of infant play in a captive group of lowland gorillas (*Gorilla gorilla gorilla*). *American Journal of Primatology* 1, 1, 65-72.

Hoff, M. P., Nadler, R. D., and Maple, T. L. 1982. Control role of an adult male in a captive group of lowland gorillas. *Folia Primatologica* 38, 1, 72-85.

Hoff, M. P., Nadler, R. D., and Maple, T. L. 1983. Maternal transport and infant motor development in a captive group of lowland gorillas. *Primates* 24, 1, 77-85.

Hoff, M.P. and Maple, T.L. 1995. Post occupancy modification of a lowland gorilla enclosure at Zoo Atlanta. *International Zoo Yearbook*, 34, 153-160.

Hoff, M.P., Hoff, K.T., Horton, L.C., and Maple, T.L. 1996. Behavioral effects of changing group membership among captive lowland gorillas. *Zoo Biology* 15, 4, 383-393.

Hoff, M. P., Nadler, R. D., and Maple, T. L. 1998. Behavioral response of a western lowland gorilla group to the loss of the silverback male. *International Zoo Yearbook* 36, 1, 90-96.

Hornaday, W. T. 1915. Gorillas past and present. *Zoological Society Bulletin of New York* 18, 1181-1185.

Jackson, D. W. 1990. Landscaping in hostile environments. *International Zoo Yearbook* 29, 10-15.

King, J.E. and Figueredo, A.J. 1997. The five-factor model plus dominance in chimpanzee personality. *Journal of Research In Personality* 31, 257-271.

Kirk, J. 2010. *Kingdom Under Glass*. New York, Picador, Henry Holt & Company.

McFarland, K. L. (2007). *Ecology of Cross River Gorillas on Afi Mountain, Cross River State, Nigeria*. Ph.D. thesis, City University of New York.

Maple, T. L. 1974. Sexually aroused self-aggression in a socialized adult male monkey. *Archives of Sexual Behavior*, 3, 5, 471-475.

Maple, T. L. 1979a. Great apes in captivity: The good, the bad, and the ugly. In Erwin, J., Mitchell, G., and Maple, T. L. (Eds), *Captivity and Behavior*. New York, Van Nostrand Reinhold Co.

Maple, T. L. 1979b. Primate psychology in historical perspective. In Erwin, J., et al., (Eds), *Captivity and Behavior*. New York, Van Nostrand Reinhold.

Maple, T. L. 1980. *Orang-utan Behavior*. New York, Van Nostrand Reinhold Co.

Maple, T. L. 1981. Audubon's apes move uptown. *At the Zoo* 2, 4, 4-7.

Maple, T. L. 2001. The power of one. In Rabb, G. (Ed.), *The Apes: Challenges for the 21st Century: Conference Proceedings*. Chicago, Chicago Zoological Society, pp. 208-209.

Maple, T. L. 2019. *Beyond Animal Welfare: The Art and Science of Wellness*. Charleston, SC: Palmetto Publishing Group/KDP Amazon.

Maple, T. L., and Hoff, M. P. 1982. *Gorilla Behavior*. New York, Van Nostrand Reinhold Co.

Maple, T. L., and Lindburg, D. G. (Eds.). 2008. Empirical zoo: Opportunities and challenges to research in zoos and aquariums. Special Issue of *Zoo Biology* 27, 6, 431-504.

Maple, T. L., and Segura, V. 2017. Comparative psychopathology: Connecting comparative and clinical psychology. In Exploring the Intersection of Comparative and Clinical Psychology. Special Issue of the *International Journal of Comparative Psychology* 30, pp. 1-11.

Maple, T. L., and Zucker, E. L. 1978. Ethological studies of play behavior in captive great apes. In Smith, E. O. (Ed), *Social Play of Primates*. New York, Academic Press, 113-142.

Maple, T. L., Zucker, E. L., and Dennon, M. B. 1979. Cyclic proceptivity in a captive female orang-utan. *Behavioural Processes* 4, 53-59.

Maple, T.L.2021. *Atlanta's Iconic Ape: The Story of Willie B.* Fernandina Bech, FL, Red Leaf/Palmetto Publishers.

Mayhew, J., and Gomez, J-C. 2015. Gorillas with white sclera: A naturally occurring variation in a morphological trait linked to social cognitive functions. *American Journal of Primatology* 77, 8, 869-877. https://doi.org/10.1002/ajp.22411.

Miller, C. I., Schwartz, A. M., Barnhart, J. S., Jr., and Bell, M. D. 1999. Chronic hypertension with subsequent congestive heart failure in a western lowland gorilla. *Journal of Zoo and Wildlife Medicine* 30, 2, 262-267.

Montgomery, G. M. 2009. Infinite loneliness: The life and times of Miss Congo. *Endeavor* 33, 3, 100-105.

Nadler, R.D. 1977. Sexual behavior of captive orangutans. *Archives of Sexual Behavior* 6, 457-475.

Ogden, J. J., Finlay, T. W., and Maple, T. L. 1990. Gorilla adaptations to naturalistic environments. *Zoo Biology* 9, 2, 107-121.

Ogden, J.J., Lindburg, D.G. and Maple, T.L. 1993. Preferences for structural environmental features in captive lowland gorillas. *Zoo Biology* 12, 4, 381-396.

Ogden, J.J., Lindburg, D.G. and Maple, T.L. 1993. The effects of ecologically-relevant sounds on the cognitive and affective behavior of zoo visitors. *Curator* 36, 2, 147-156.

Ogden, J.J., Lindburg, D.G., and Maple, T.L. 1994. A preliminary study of the effects of ecologically-relevant sounds on the behaviour of captive lowland gorillas. *Applied Animal Behaviour Science* 39, 2, 163-176.

Ogden, J.J., Carpanzano, C. and Maple, T.L.1994. Immersion exhibits: how are they proving as educational exhibits? *Annual Conference Proceedings.* Wheeling W.VA, American Zoo and Aquarium Association, 224-228.

Perez, S. E., Sherwood, C. C., Cranfield, M. R., Erwin, J. M., Mudakikwa, A., Hof, P. R., and Mufson, E. J. 2016. Early Alzheimer's disease-type pathology in the frontal cortex of wild mountain gorillas. *Neurobiology of Aging* 39, 195-201.

Plotnik, J. M., de Waal, F. B. M., and Reiss, D. 2006. Self-recognition in an Asian elephant. *Proceedings of the National Academy of Sciences* 103, 45, 10753-10757. DOI: 10.1073/pnas.0608062103.

Pollick, A.S. and de Waal, F.B.M. 2007. Ape gestures and language evolution. PNAS. DOI: 10.1073/pnas.0702624104.

Popovich, D.G. and Dierenfeld, F.S. 1997. Gorilla Nutrition. In Ogden, J. and Wharton, D. (Eds.) *Management of Gorillas in Captivity, Husbandry Manual, Species Survival Plan.* Wheeling, W.Va., American Association of Zoos and Aquariums.

Reiss, B. F., Ross, S., Lyerly, S. B., and Birch, H. G. 1949. The behavior of two captive specimens of the lowland gorilla, *Gorilla gorilla gorilla* (Savage and Wyman). *Zoological Science Contributions of the New York Zoological Society* 34 (PL 3), 111-118.

Reynolds, R. 2000. Unpublished manuscript.

Savage-Rumbaugh, E. S. 1986. *Ape Language from Conditioned Response to Symbol.* New York, Columbia University Press.

Schaller, G. B. 1963. *The Mountain Gorilla: Ecology and Behavior.* Chicago, University of Chicago Press.

Schwartz, B. L., Meissner, C. A., Hoffman, M., Evans, S., and Frazier, L. D. 2004. Event memory and misinformation effects in a gorilla (*Gorilla gorilla gorilla*). *Animal Cognition* 7, 2, 93-100.

Smithgall, C. 2008. *I Took the Fork.* Marietta, GA, Mana Publications.

Sommer, R. 1972. What do we learn at the zoo? *Natural History.*

Sommer, R. 1974. *Tight Spaces.* Englewood Cliffs, NJ, Prentice-Hall.

Sommer, R. 2008. Development of the zoological garden and mental hospital. *American Journal of Orthopsychiatry* 78, 3, 378-382.

Stern, L. 2020. What can bonobos teach us about the nature of language? *Smithsonian*, July/August.

Stoinski, T. 2020. How the hard lesson of Covid could help gorillas. *Project Planet*, CNN Editorial.

Stoinski, T.S., Hoff, M.P., Lukas, K.E. and Maple, T.L. 2001. A behavioral comparison of two captive all-male gorilla groups. *Zoo Biology* 20, 1, 27-40.

Stoinski, T. S., Kuhar, C. W., Lukas, K. E., and Maple, T. L. 2004. Social dynamics of captive western lowland gorillas living in all-male groups. *Behaviour* 141, 169-195.

Stoinski, T. S., Lukas, K. E., Kuhar, C. W., and Maple, T. L. 2004. Factors influencing the formation and maintenance of all-male gorilla groups in captivity. *Zoo Biology* 23, 2, 189-203.

Tarou, L. R., Bloomsmith, M. A., Hoff, M. P., Erwin, J. M., and Maple, T. L. 2002. The behavior of aged great apes. In Erwin, J. M., and Hof, P. R. (Eds), *Aging in Nonhuman Primates*, Vol. 31. Basel, Karger, 209-231.

Tutin, C.E.G. and Fernandez, M. 1993. Composition of the diet of chimpanzees and comparisons with that of sympatric gorillas in the Lope Reserve, Gabon. *American Journal of Primatology* 30, 195-211.

Vonk, J., and MacDonald, S. E. 2002. Natural concepts in a juvenile gorilla (*Gorilla gorilla gorilla*) at three levels of abstraction. *Journal of the Experimental Analysis of Behavior* 78, 3, 315-332.

Ward, J. 2021. The gorilla who was brought up as a boy in an English village. *History of Yesterday*, February 2021.

Warner, J. 1998. Aunt adopts baby gorilla at Zoo Atlanta after staff intervenes. *Atlanta Journal-Constitution*, October 23.

Weiss, A., Gartner, M. C., Gold, K. C., and Stoinski, T. S. 2014. Extraversion predicts longer survival in gorillas: An 18-year longitudinal study. *Proceedings of the Royal Society*, 1-5.

Wilson, M. L., Boesch, C., and Wrangham, R. W. 2014. Lethal aggression in *Pan* is better explained by adaptive strategies than human impacts. *Nature* 513, 414-417.

Wilson, M. L., and Elicker, J. G. 1976. Establishment, maintenance, and behavior of free-ranging chimpanzees on Ossabaw Island, Georgia, USA. *Primates* 17, 451-473.

Wilson, S. F. 1982. Environmental influences on the activity of captive apes. *Zoo Biology* 1, 3, 201-209.

Wineman, J., and Choi, Y. K. 1991. Spatial/visual properties of zoo exhibition. *Curator* 34, 4, 4-15.

Wineman, J., Piper, C., and Maple, T. L. 1996. Zoos in transition: Enriching conservation education for a new generation. *Curator* 39, 2, 94-101.

Winslow, S., Ogden, J. J., and Maple, T. L. 1992. Socialization of an adult male gorilla *(G. gorilla gorilla)*. *International Zoo Yearbook* 31, 221-225.

Woodford, M. H., Butynski, T. M., and Karesh, W. B. 2002. Habituating the great apes: The disease risks. *Oryx* 36, 2, 153-160.

Yerkes, R. M. 1916. Provision for the study of monkeys and apes. *Science* 43, 231-234.

Yerkes, R. M. 1925. *Almost Human*. New York, Century.

Yerkes, R. M. 1927. The mind of a gorilla. *Genetic Psychology Monographs* 2, 1-193.

Yerkes, R.M. 1943. *Chimpanzees. A Laboratory Colony*. New Haven, Yale University Press.

Yerkes, R. M., and Yerkes, A. W. 1929. *The Great Apes: A Study of Anthropoid Life*. New Haven, Yale University Press.

Zucker, E.L., Mitchell, G. and Maple, T.L. 1978. Adult male- offspring play interactions in a captive group of orang-utans. *Primates* 19, 2, 379-384.

Appendix 1. Maple, T. and Hoff, M.P. Remembering Willie B. Op-Ed for Father's Day. Appendix 2: Maple, T. The Power of One.

REMEMBERING WILLIE B. ON FATHER'S DAY

Terry L. Maple & Michael P. Hoff

Atlanta lost one of its leading examples of fatherhood with the death of Willie B. on February 3, 2000. He was 41 years old on the occasion of his passing, the oldest gorilla to sire offspring in North America. His story is a living metaphor for the resilience of the zoo itself, a 25-year transformation from industry pariah to global leadership. My newest book, *Atlanta's Iconic Ape: The Story of Willie B.,* will be published in time for the Christmas season. If the reader examines carefully the great silverback's story, his life is alive with lessons for all of us.

Given the poverty of his early years at the zoo, Willie B. was the original "comeback kid". As he endured the stressors in his captive life, he proved to all of us that no situation is so dire that it cannot be overcome. The zoo had to learn to persevere from Willie B.'s trials and tribulations. In the end, somehow, he reached his full potential, and we had to do the same.

His capture in Africa was brutally executed by hunters with no concern for casualties. There was no public record of the hunt, but the first casualty of such encounters was almost always the dominant patriarch of the group. At the age of two, Willie B. lost his father and his mother before he even knew them. His arduous translocation to America threatened his very life, but he managed to survive and cope with the demands of captivity. In Atlanta, he was given the name of the city's charismatic mayor, William, B. Hartsfield, who governed for twenty-five years. Mayor Hartsfield's personal interest in the little gorilla helped to raise his profile.

In Willie's adolescence, with few exceptions, America's zoological parks were substandard examples of "hard architecture". Confined alone in a small concrete, steel, and tile enclosure, his social life was comprised of interacting at a distance with his devoted keeper, Charles Horton. With almost no social experience with his own kind, Willie's opportunity to become a silverback took many years before it became a priority for city fathers. Mediocrity was not enough to motivate reforms but a management scandal threatened the good reputation of the business community, and citizens soon rallied to the cause. Working with prominent business leaders, Mayor Andrew Young led the way to an emerging public/private partnership that proved to be the right governance model for the zoo.

The model was complete when the Ford Motor Company stepped up to provide essential private funding for a new gorilla exhibit. The design team comprised of world class zoo architects, Coe and Lee, and highly regarded local construction firms produced the Ford African Rainforest. When it opened in 1988, it was the most advanced gorilla exhibit in the world.

The key to Willie's future was the loan of thirteen gorillas from Emory University's Yerkes National Primate Research Center. A critical mass sufficient to encourage breeding, it was the most important loan of endangered animals in the history of North American zoos. With so many gorillas available to zoo managers, it didn't take long for Willie B. to get his chance to interact with his own kind. He proved to be a quick study and got along well with every female who was introduced to him.

Willie B. sired five offspring, four females and one male who we dubbed "Willie B. Junior". Junior still lives at the zoo where he is the resident silverback in his own family group. Because we studied Willie B. and the other Yerkes gorillas, we know that he was an unusually doting father.

He was a strong role model for his offspring, actively controlling conflict among the adult females, but the youngsters found him irresistible and did their best to engage him in bouts of play. More than any of the other silverbacks at the zoo, Willie was accommodating in play. He clearly liked to interact with the little gorillas and he did so in a gentle, tolerant way. Unusual for a silverback, he even let them share his food.

Willie B. was an inspiring father figure. He overcame so many obstacles in his life to become the successful silverback we hoped for. In nonhuman primates, young animals are typically scarred for life when they are raised without a mother and father. This is why it is so important to establish normal social groups for each species in human care. People too suffer when they are raised in households with absentee mothers and fathers. Fathers are particularly important to young men as they act as a constraint on aggression.

Mike and I were fortunate to grow up in stable households with strong fathers. Mike had four brothers and I had two. They all turned out well and we give our father's much of the credit for our disciplined approach to our lives and careers. Mike has a grown daughter and I have three. Our paternal experience has been the highlight of our lives. Like Willie B., we paid a lot of attention to them when they were little and stayed involved in their life as they grew up. They too turned out well. For gorillas and for people, the family is an essential feature of a full life.

What we learned from Willie B. is worth repeating. Resilience is always possible. Be patient and tolerant of others. Avoid aggression in the family. Become the social glue that strengthens the family bonds. Vigorously defend your family against all adversaries.

Although Willie B. is no longer with us, gorilla families are still thriving at Zoo Atlanta. We recommend that they be studied and appreciated for what they can teach us. On Father's Day each year it is a good time to remember Willie B. by widely sharing his remarkable story. Like Willie B., no matter what comes our way, we will not be discouraged or defeated.

Terry L. Maple

THE POWER OF ONE

Terry L. Maple[1]

Willie B., a 41-year-old lowland gorilla, passed away in Atlanta, Georgia, on February 2, 2000. Nearly 8,000 people attended his memorial service held at Zoo Atlanta a few days after his death. The loss of Willie B. deeply affected Atlanta citizens who accepted him as a valued personal friend. We mourned his passing; but we also celebrated his extraordinary life and legacy.

His 39 years of residence at the zoo, unique personality, and the remarkable story of his life combined to elevate him to the level of celebrity. He was frequently lampooned in political cartoons in the local newspapers. His image was featured on the most prominent wall of the celebrity-festooned Palm Restaurant at the Atlanta Swisshotel. *Fundraising Magazine, Atlanta Magazine*, and many other local and regional publications sought his grizzled visage for their covers. The nickname of the Atlanta "Silverbacks" professional soccer team was inspired by the owner's exposure to Willie B. His birthday had become a really big deal, especially as he extended his record as the oldest captive gorilla to sire offspring. He was, as we like to say, "zoobiquitous." The zoo director had come to believe that Willie B. would live (and breed) forever.

Captured in Africa (we believe the location was somewhere in Cameroon) in 1961, he arrived at the Atlanta Zoo in May, having spent a few months with peers at the Kansas City home of his captor, Deets Pickett. Old-timers remember that a first "Willie B." died in his first year of residence. Both were named for longtime Atlanta mayor William B. Hartsfield. Atlanta's international airport is also named for Hartsfield, but I suspect the great ape has been the superior legacy.

In *ZOOM Magazine* (spring '98), Zoo Atlanta's quarterly membership publication, I had the opportunity to write about my first introduction to Willie B. in September of 1975. As I recalled:

> *"On my first morning in Atlanta, I arrived early for a tour of the zoo. Willie B. was sitting in a corner of his blue-tile cage. Behind bars and glass, he was isolated and effectively distanced from his adoring public ... Willie B. was in jail through no fault of his own. He was in the prime of his life, just 17 years old. He was handsome, strong and capable, and completely alone."*

Willie B. spent 28 years at the zoo without contact with his own kind, but he developed close relationships with his devoted caretakers who played with him when he was young, and later (from a safe distance) provided him affection and attention. Over the years, his medical care was considerably upgraded. At the end, he was attended by the zoo veterinarian Dr. Rita McManamon and a team of esteemed cardiologists and other medical experts from Emory University. We spared no expense in meeting his needs.

As Willie B. prospered, so did the zoo. Our partnership with the Yerkes Primate Research Center of Emory University was the first dramatic step toward the revitalization of Zoo Atlanta. The acquisition of 13 gorillas, on loan from Yerkes, enabled the zoo to approach the Ford Motor Company for financial support. We dreamed of building a gorilla exhibit second to none, a simulation of natural habitats in Central and West Africa. As Ford executives carefully scrutinized our plans, the charisma of Willie B. helped us close the deal.

Willie B.'s life changed dramatically in 1988 with the opening of the Ford African Rainforest exhibit. Designed by Jon Charles Coe, the benchmark facility was intended for the population of gorillas, presented to the public in four separate habitats. When Willie B. set foot on grass, his lifelong fans were gathered to witness it in person and on live television. There wasn't a dry eye in the house! In the 12 years since we opened the exhibit, 12 offspring have been produced, all but one raised by its mother, and all of them thriving in complex social groups.

From the beginning, Willie B. was housed at the apex of the exhibitry representing the natural phenomenon of "solitary" gorillas. He was solitary in this way for less than a year when we introduced him to two females on May 31, 1989. Given his history of isolation from other gorillas, his emergent social skills were nothing short of remarkable. Soon he was so successful that we moved him to the much larger habitat, and three more females were added to his harem to take advantage of his fertility and his enthusiasm.

Five offspring later, Willie B. was leading a silverback's life. He occupied a complex (and fully functional) family group of four adult females and five offspring (Kudzoo, Olympia, Sukari, Kidogo, Lulu) from one to six years in age. He was arguably the most successful silverback in America. At 41, he was the oldest gorilla to sire offspring in North America, contesting the world title with a male in Zurich of comparable age. (I wasn't sure who was older, but the issue is now moot.) Who knows how long he would have continued his prolific record had he survived to 50 and beyond? His continuing fecundity was about to set up an interesting debate within the Gorilla Species Survival Plan. Should we risk over-representation to find out how long male gorillas can continue to sire offspring? I am confident that the committee would have elected to continue our experiment in reproductive longevity.

So how do you celebrate the life of such an extraordinary creature? We could think of no one better to deliver his eulogy than former U.N. ambassador and former mayor of Atlanta Reverend Andrew Young. On two days' notice he agreed to participate, speaking volumes about his respect for Willie B. Mayor Young was eloquent when he said:

> *"...when a little baby gorilla was found in Africa, people loved him and they named him for the mayor that they loved, and he had the same kind of impact on the city that the mayor did. We looked at him in his cage and we knew that he didn't belong there. He was brought here into captivity but he found a way to appeal to our hearts so that we were moved to find ways to set him free. And in setting him free, perhaps we set ourselves free to help us learn that we can live together in peace with all of the animals that God had created."*

160

Willie B. lived large, and I knew that his death would be gargantuan. It was bigger than that. In my career, composed of a multitude of peak experiences, nothing compares to that moment when our small delegation of six speakers addressed the massive crowd that had assembled to bid him adieu. Such love. Such sadness. How he touched the people. It was exhilarating to contemplate his affect on humanity. Once again, Willie B. had made us cry together.

I believe that Willie B.'s life proves the value and importance of the zoo. In such places, people connect with wildlife. In time, we personalize the animals and develop profound relationships that are enduring and powerful. When they die, we mourn their passing. We are truly diminished with their passing, and the effects linger. It is, plain and simple, a painful experience. I miss him as much as any person I have ever known. For so many Georgians, Willie B. was family.

Willie B. clearly demonstrates the power and the impact of one individual's wonderful life. He enriched us; he inspired; and he changed us forever. If the power of this gorilla can be harnessed and properly applied, perhaps we can change the world.

ABOUT THE AUTHOR

Professor Terry L. Maple spent thirty years in academia on the faculty at Emory University and the Georgia Institute of Technology. He retired from Tech as Elizabeth Smithgall Watts Professor Emeritus. He enjoyed a parallel career as a zoological executive, hired in 1984 by City of Atlanta Mayor Andrew Young to lead the privatization of Atlanta's city zoo. While reimagining and creating one of North America's most naturalistic zoological parks, Professor Maple and his students published more than 250 books and papers during his eighteen years at the helm of the zoo. He spent an additional six years as the CEO of Palm Beach Zoo. He was the founding editor of the scientific journal *Zoo Biology*, and he was the first recipient of the Lifetime Contributions to Animal Welfare Award presented by the Association of Zoos and Aquariums (AZA) in 2018. In 2013, Springer-Verlag published *Zoo Animal Welfare* (coauthored by B. Perdue). His most recent book is *Beyond Animal Welfare: The Art and Science of Wellness* (Palmetto, 2019). As an organizational consultant, he was honored by Division 13 of the American Psychological Association with the Harry Levinson Award for his exceptional ability to integrate a wide range of psychological theory and concepts so managers may create more effective, healthy, and humane organizations. His honors for leadership include the Distinguished Psychologist in Management award presented by the Society of Psychologists in Management (SPIM). He is currently affiliated with the Jacksonville Zoo and Gardens, the University of North Florida, and Florida Atlantic University. Professor Maple and his wife Addie have three daughters and four grandchildren.

Made in the USA
Middletown, DE
16 September 2022

10625815R00097